Let the Evidence Speak !

Let the Evidence Speak!

creation or evolution

Buryl R. Eads

 Peachtree Publishers, Ltd.

Published by
PEACHTREE PUBLISHERS, LTD.
494 Armour Circle, N. E.
Atlanta, Georgia 30324

Cover design by Joan Stoliar

Library of Congress Cataloging in Publication Data
Eads, Buryl R.
    Let the evidence speak!
    Includes bibliographical references.
    1. Bible and evolution. I. Title.
BS659.E22   213   79-17377
ISBN 0-931948-02-9

Grateful appreciation is extended to the following for permission to quote from their copyrighted materials:

Presbyterian and Reformed Publishing Company, Nutley, NJ

Institute for Creation Research, San Diego, CA

Creation-Life Publishers, San Diego, CA

Random House, Inc., New York, NY

Harcourt Brace Jovanovich, New York, NY

TIME, The Weekly Newsmagazine, New York, NY

Baker Book House, Grand Rapids, MI

Concordia Publishing House, St. Louis, MO

Collier's Encyclopedia, MacMillan Educational Corporation, New York, NY

John Wiley and Sons, New York, NY

Nature, MacMillan Journals Ltd., London, England

Griffith Observatory, Los Angeles, CA

W. H. Freeman and Company, San Francisco, CA

American Scientist, New Haven, CT

Journal of Geological Education, University of Wisconsin, Kenosha, WI

Science, Washington, DC

The University of Chicago Press, Chicago, IL

George Allen and Unwin Ltd., Hemel Hempstead, England

CONTENTS

To

Sharon

without whose patience, understanding and encouragement, this
book may never have been written.

Foreword

A few years ago a friend offered me a challenge: "Prove evolution and I will also believe it." At the time I was an evolutionist, having been well trained in the doctrine of evolution. But as I began my research into the validity of the evidence that is often used to "prove" evolution, I soon discovered that evolution cannot be proved, is not subject to observation or experimentation, and is in violation of several major biological and physical laws.

There is, however, considerable evidence that attests to flaws in the theory of evolution. I have included some of this evidence in this book. It is possible that this will be the first time you have been made aware that evidence contrary to the theory of evolution exists. Unless you are acquainted with the works of such men as Drs. Henry Morris, Duane Gish, John Whitcomb, Richard Bliss, Thomas Barnes, and Melvin Cook, then the chances are that you are not acquainted with the other side of the evidence. These men have considered the evidence and no longer accept the theory of evolution. You have the right to hear that same evidence!

I am convinced that the whole truth of evolution has not been told, because evidence that refutes the theory of evolution is seldom ever reported. A university professor, an acclaimed evolutionist, once admitted to me that he cannot consider as scientific any evidence that refutes evolution. No wonder evolution has become so widely accepted today!

This book considers only a small part of the evidence that supports special creation. Although it is not a comprehensive study on the question of creation or evolution, I hope you will come to the conclusion that the creationists have just as solid a footing scientifically, if not actually more so, than do the evolutionists. You will have to be the judge of that.

If you are an evolutionist, or theistic-evolutionist, the question I would ask you to consider carefully as you read this book is, what evidence do I believe exists that supports the theory of evolution? Before you begin, take the time to make a list of the evidence you believe proves evolution. Ten items would be sufficient. Place your list at the end of the book. When you finish, review your list and see how your ten items held up.

I accepted the challenge and now I offer you the same challenge to *prove evolution if you can*. I believe you will be surprised and pleased at the personal satisfaction you will gain from your investigation. Let this book be the starting point in your search for the truth.

Buryl R. Eads
Oceanside, California
January 10, 1979

Let
the
Evidence
Speak !

1. BEHIND THE EVOLUTIONARY THEORY

The theory of evolution holds that all living things arose by a natural, physical process from a single primeval cell, which in turn arose through spontaneous generation from a dead, inanimate world. It is believed this process of evolution has always occurred and through it the primeval cell has developed into the great variety of life forms in existence today.

Many people are convinced that evolution is the natural process through which not only human beings came into existence but all life forms as well. Even the universe is considered to be the product of the evolutionary process. Evolution has become so widely accepted that many consider it a sign of ignorance not to believe it. A very popular source states that evolution can be denied only by "an abandonment of reason." This same source then goes on to explain that it is one thing to be told "and want to believe" in the creation story, but another thing to be told "and have to believe" in the theory of evolution. In actuality there is not a single, observable biological process that is dependent upon the theory of evolution.

Julian Huxley, in *Issues in Evolution* (1960), said that "Darwin removed the whole idea of God as Creator of organisms from the sphere of rational discussion." Darwin believed that no supernatural designer was needed; that natural selection could account for all known life forms.

Many people are surprised to discover that there are people in science careers who do not accept the theory of evolution. I have often heard comments that go something like this: "How can you be a biologist and not believe in evolution?" Well, I am a biologist and I *do not* believe in evolution. This was not so when I graduated from college. I had been trained in the evolutionary doctrine, and I supported it completely. I taught it to my students as a fact, just as it had been taught to me.

The major portion of this book is a review of my research into the validity of the theory of evolution. You may not agree with my findings, but I am certain that you will agree that the whole truth about evolution has not been told.

It may be true that many scientifically-minded people support the theory of evolution, but just because a majority believes in something does not mean it is necessarily true. At one time in the not-too-distant past, most leading medical authorities believed that malaria was caused by "bad air" from a swamp; that certain illnesses were caused by "bad blood," and the best cure was to get rid of some of that blood; and that washing hands before performing surgery was a waste of the surgeon's time. Eventually the evidence proved otherwise. The key to a scientific theory is not how many people believe in the theory or how educated they may be, but in the credibility of the evidence that supports the theory.

Scientific Bias

A very common misconception about scientists is that they are totally objective in their interpretation of evidence. "Science deals in total objectivity and is unbiased, therefore scientists are also totally objective and unbiased." Unfortunately this is not always the case. My own personal experience has been that most scientists trained in the evolutionary line of thinking are not willing to consider evidence contrary to their training. I have spoken with science educators in many areas, and I have not found them generally receptive to evidence that refutes evolution. As a matter of fact, I have found many of them to be quite "human" and quite biased. Some have even become rather hostile at the suggestion that there is an alternative to evolution.

Once when I had an opportunity to share some of the evidence that suggests the earth is much younger than 4.5 billion years, I was interrupted when the person to whom I was speaking stood up and said, "Stop! This kind of evidence is completely against my grain of thinking!" On another occasion the interruption went like this: "Look, I know what you are trying to say, but I am not interested in that kind of evidence."

No wonder so many believe in evolution. If a person is not willing to consider evidence that contradicts evolution, then it is easy to accept and teach evolution as a fact. While the scientific method implores scientists to be open-minded and not reject valid evidence, it seems that the pride of their training quickly blinds them.

Dr. John W. Klotz reported a study done by Dr. E. G. Boring, Professor Emeritus of Psychology at Harvard (see "Cognitive Dissonance," *Science*, 1964), that revealed the problem many scientists have in giving up a belief even though evidence has proven it to be false.

> (Boring) believes, and most historians of science will agree with him, that scientists cling tenaciously to conceptual schemes even in the light of mounting evidence against them . . . . Yet scientists form an emotional attachment to these hypotheses and theories which they have come to accept. There is a pride of authorship, a fierce loyalty to the conceptual scheme which the individual has espoused.[1]

I have attempted to set up debates between creationists and evolutionists and have found the problem even more obvious. I have listened to scientists indoctrinated in evolution explain their reluctance to participate in the debate because, in simple English, anyone who disagrees with them cannot be considered scientific.

Many scientists often become quite egocentric concerning their personal area of study. Dr. Philip H. Abelson wrote an article entitled "Bigotry in Science" that appeared in *Science* in 1964 in which he stated:

> One of the most astonishing characteristics of scientists is that some of them are plain, old-fashioned bigots. Their zeal has a fanatical, egocentric quality characterized by disdain and intolerance for anyone or any value not associated with a special area of intellectual activity.[2]

Outside Empirical Science

It is not an easy thing for a concept to become a scientific theory. To do this a concept must be observable and capable of yielding quantitative measurement. It must also be capable of verification through additional experiments and repeated observations. That is what empirical science is all about; the search for truth that is supported by observable, testable and undisputed evidence.

Admittedly for this very reason, special creation can never be treated as a scientific theory. Creation is not subject to observation or measurement. It is simply not taking place now according to Genesis 2:1–2. Furthermore, it would be impossible to devise an experiment that could demonstrate creation. This is not to say, however, that creation did not occur but rather that it is outside and beyond the realm of empirical science.

And for the same reason, the process of evolution should not be treated as a scientific theory because it cannot be observed and therefore does not yield quantitative evidence. Dr. Theodosius Dobzhansky, a leading proponent for evolution, admitted that evolution is simply not capable of being observed because it occurs much too slowly for the lifetime of any human experimenter. He concluded that the applicability of the experimental method to the study of evolution is severely restricted.[3]

Of course, the fact that evolution is too slow a process to be observed does not disprove evolution but simply places it, along with creation, outside the empirical sciences. Evolutionists throughout the land have loudly protested efforts to present special creation as a possible explanation of the origin of life because they do not consider it to be within the realm of science. However, evolution, which also lies outside empirical science, has been given an exemption to this rule. This special allowance is a serious infringement upon the philosophical and academic freedom necessary for the preservation of our educational system.

Many people who reject evolution in their own personal belief do not seem to be overly concerned about the universal teaching of evolution, although I believe most adults actually prefer that both creation and evolution be presented.

The California State Board of Education called for changes to be made in all science texts so that they would include all theories, including creation, on the origin of life. This ruling was to have taken effect by 1974. According to this board, when one theory is presented the other must also be presented, since neither is capable of being proved. An examination of science texts within California will quickly show that this ruling is not being upheld.

What Is a Scientific Theory?

A scientific theory is much more than just a hunch or guess as to the answer to a problem. The word "science" comes from the Latin *scientia* and means knowledge that is founded on observation, study and experiment.

Empirical science is concerned with the manner and direction taken in solving a problem. The very first step is to identify the problem correctly. The next step is to develop an hypothesis, or "educated guess," as to what the possible solution to the problem may be. The hypothesis must be logical and in harmony with other known facts. It must be capable of experimentation that will yield observable results. Repeated experimentation and observations will give further validity to the first findings. From the results, a conclusion may be drawn as to the accuracy of the hypothesis. If the results support the hypothesis, then the hypothesis may become a theory. Scientifically then, a theory is an explanation for a natural phenomenon that is supported by observation and experimentation.

Scientific Method of Inquiry

First: Identification of the problem
Second: Development of an hypothesis
   a) a logical explanation based on previous knowledge
   b) experimentation and observation
   c) results of the experiment
   d) conclusion based on the results
Third: Scientific theory
   an explanation supported by experimentation and observation

An excellent example of a scientific theory is the *cell theory* developed by Virchow and Schwann in 1839. This theory has become the very foundation for biogenesis, or the understanding that life can only come from life. The cell theory is divided into three parts:

1. The cell is the basic unit of life
2. All living things are made of cells
3. All cells come only from pre-existing cells

After more than a century of research, the cell theory has been upheld by experimentation and observation. The cell theory is not just a scientific hunch, but rather a scientific fact. Evolution states that the first living cell came from an inanimate world. The cell theory states that cells can only come from pre-existing cells. The two are in conflict and only the latter is supported by scientific evidence.

Evolution has failed to meet the criteria that would allow it to become a scientific theory. In summary, the following can be said of evolution:

1. Its process is not capable of being observed
2. It is not subject to experimentation
3. It is not supported by evidence
4. It contradicts many biological processes
5. Its acceptance rests upon pure belief

Dr. Paul Ehrlich, a leading evolutionist, has concluded that evolution "is thus outside the empirical science." Harvard professor George Wald stated that he believes in evolution simply because without it modern biologists are left with nothing.[4]

Where's the Evidence?

It would seem that any theory as well promoted as evolution should have a substantial collection of very convincing evidence by now. Actually, the evidence that has been produced—natural selection, genetic mutation and the fossil record—tends to disprove the theory of evolution rather than to confirm it. Evolution is not based on evidence, or for that matter, even logic. This was evident as early as 1929 when the outstanding British biologist, Dr. D. M. S. Watson, pointed out that evolution was more an attack on special creation than an introduction of a breakthrough in science. He stated that evolution is universally accepted not because of logically coherent evidence, "but because the only alternative, special creation, is clearly incredible."[5]

The theory of evolution is based upon the assumption that special creation is impossible. In other words, *ex nihilo* (out of nothing) is more preferred than *ex Deo* (out of God). But this concept can only be true in the minds of those who make the assumption that there is no God. If there is no God, then obviously there can be no special creation. But if this *assumption* (that special creation could not have occurred because there is no God) is the foundation for the belief in the theory of evolution, then evolution can hardly be considered scientific or even logical. More accurately it should be called the *assumption of evolution*.

Loren Eisely, in *The Immense Journey*, points out that evolution has not been proved:

> With the failure of these many efforts, science was left in the somewhat embarrassing position of having to postulate theories of living origins which it could not demonstrate. After having chided the theologian for his reliance on myth and miracle, science found itself in the unenviable position of having to create a mythology of its own: namely, the assumption that what, after long effort could not be proved to take place today had, in truth, taken place in the primeval past.[6]

Extralogical Reasoning

A professor once explained that "evolution is based on change; change is a fact, and therefore evolution must also be a fact." This kind of reasoning has led to what Dr. Thomas Barnes, professor of physics at the University of Texas, calls *extralogical error*:

> In evolution, an extralogical error occurs when phenomena with observable limits are cited as evidence in support of an unbounded proposition.[7]

Such illogical reasoning should not be permitted within scientific circles, but it is often present concerning evolution. Evolution is a fact only in the minds of those who wish to believe it is a fact. It is amazing that after all the years scientists have toiled in the various disciplines, evolution has not become a scientific law but rather remains a theory—or even less, an hypothesis. It is not a law and should not even be a scientific theory because it lacks the necessary evidence to allow it to become anything more than a working hypothesis.

Julian Huxley, in the concluding speech at the Darwinian Centennial Convention at the University of Chicago, in 1959, praised evolution not because of any evidence that supports it, but because it simply provides a method to explain existing life without acknowledging a Divine Creator. Because of evolution, Huxley felt there was no longer room for God. He was convinced that the earth evolved and was not the result of special creation. He therefore stated that plants, animals and humans were all the results of evolution. Religion itself was the result of the evolutionary process: "Evolutionary man can no longer take refuge from his loneliness by creeping for shelter into the arms of a divinized father figure whom he himself has created."[8]

In *Perspectives on the News* (June, 1966) Aldous Huxley (1894–1963), British novelist and essayist, was reported as having said that it was his desire to have a world without meaning, because in such a world the philosopher would be absolutely free to do as he wanted to: "For myself, the philosophy of meaninglessness was essentially an instrument of liberation, sexual and political."

If evolution is the naturalistic process to which we owe our origin, then we must look at the world in a completely new perspective—a world without purpose or meaning. Life would be nothing more than a freak accident of some natural laws that are completely unknown today. But as stated earlier, the validity of a scientific theory is not how many people believe in the theory or how educated they might be; it is in the evidence that supports the theory.

Creation: An Acceptable Alternative

There is an acceptable alternative to the nondirectional, nonpurposive, mechanistic theory of evolution: namely, special creation. Many who reject special creation have done so because they are unaware of the preponderance of evidence that supports it.

Creationists feel that much of the evidence concerning origins is overwhelmingly in favor of special creation. All they are asking is an equal opportunity to present their case. Those who then choose to reject creation as an explanation of the origin of life will do so because they have examined the evidence, not because they were simply told not to believe it.

Creationists can present their case on a scientific level as has been demonstrated by the many lectures and debates that have occurred on many major campuses throughout the nation. In 1975 there were over 60 such lectures and debates in leading colleges and universities which were attended by thousands of concerned individuals. In almost every case the evolutionary supporters were surprised at the scientific, non-Biblical approach of the creationists.

Perhaps you may be thinking, "But I was taught that evolution is true and supported by all kinds of evidence." If your science teacher was like the majority of science teachers, the theory of evolution was taught to him just about the same way in which he taught it to you.

More likely than not, his acceptance of evolution was *not* based on a careful study of the evidence for or against evolution. Most educators are not even aware that there is such evidence.

Evolution is taught as a dogma, accepted by "most enlightened people" because the "only alternative, special creation, is clearly incredible." Evolution is simply the assumption that an unobservable process believed possible, but not capable of being proved, has actually taken place. According to Dr. Ehrlich: "No one can think of ways in which to test it. . . . (Evolutionary ideas) have become part of an evolutionary dogma accepted by most of us as part of our training."[9]

Evolution On Trial

On July 10, 1925, the teaching of evolution in the public schools was given a test trial when the State of Tennessee decided to prosecute John T. Scopes for teaching his high school students that man descended from monkeys. Tennessee State Law made it "unlawful for any teacher in a state-supported school or university to teach any theory that denies the story of the Divine Creation of man as taught in the Bible, and to teach instead that man descended from a lower order of animal." The scientific world may have been ready to accept the teaching of evolution, but the general public was not.

The trial attracted international attention. The prosecution was conducted by the attorney general of Tennessee, Thomas Stewart, assisted by William Jennings Bryan. The defense was headed primarily by Clarence Darrow who maintained that the Tennessee Law was unconstitutional. In an effort to avoid a debate on the validity of evolution or creation, it is interesting to note that the testimony of Bible scholars and science experts was excluded as much as possible from the trial. Statements of scientists and noted educators were filed, however, in the record of the trial.

One piece of pro-evolutionary evidence that managed to get into the Scope's trial was a single fossil tooth believed by the evolutionists to have belonged to the "Nebraskan Man," assumed to have lived in western Nebraska several thousands of years in the past. Many evolutionists were convinced that this tooth represented a half-man, half-ape creature and was the missing link between man and ape. All this was theorized from the presence of a single tooth.

It was reasoned that in order for the Nebraskan Man to possess such a tooth, he must have had a certain type of jaw. This primitive jaw must have required a certain skull shape which eventually led to the hypothetical construction of an entire skeleton. Science experts were willing to testify as to the behavioral patterns of this missing link. But, to the embarrassment of these evolutionary experts, the Nebraskan Man eventually turned out to be neither ape nor man but an extinct peccary or pig!

John Scopes was found guilty of violating the state law and was fined $100 and lost his teaching position. Two years later the Supreme Court of Tennessee upheld that the law was constitutional but reversed the judgment against Scopes on a technicality.

Times have certainly changed since 1925. Today, John Scopes would have no problem teaching evolution. However, he might receive some criticism should he try to teach *Creationism*. Evolution has become a "sacred cow" in the scientific community and it is considered heresy to question it.

Very recently a statement signed by 180 well-known authors and scientists was sent to the nation's major school boards stressing "evolution as a principle of science" and decrying creation as a "purely religious issue." This statement was signed by such men as Linus Pauling, James Watson, Isaac Asimov, Carl Rogers and George Simpson. They objected to any attempt to present a concept of creation in the educational system because "there are no alternatives to the theory of evolution."

Many evolutionists, though claiming that there are no alternatives to the theory of evolution, readily admit that evolution is not a firmly established fact. A leading professor of psychology and human behavior at the United States International University in San Diego and an avid supporter of evolution said: "Science does not believe in absolutes anymore. It deals with statistical probabilities and the overwhelming statistical evidence favors evolution."

But do the statistical probabilities favor evolution? A group of mathematicians, all of whom are evolutionists, estimated the number of favorable mutations that would be necessary to bring about certain changes that would cause an amoeba-like organism eventually to evolve into a man. The answer turned out that the time necessary for these changes, made at random, assuming that such changes were actually possible, was billions of times longer than the assumed five billion years of the earth's history.

One of these mathematicians further stated that if the postulated "random" genetic mutations, the method through which simple life forms supposedly evolved into more complex life forms, were to be given any serious consideration from a probabilistic point of view, then "an adequate scientific theory of evolution must await the discovery and elucidation of new natural laws—physical, physicochemical, and biological."

Furthermore, not all scientists hold to the theory of evolution, but claim that when all evidence is considered, only special creation can account for the many life forms on earth and that only the creative act of a Divine Being can account for the phenomenon of life itself. The Creation Research Society lists over 550 M.S. and Ph.D. scientists as members who support creation rather than evolution.

Why Teach Origins?

Should the origin of life be taught since both creation and evolution lie outside the realm of science? Would it be just a waste of time? Hardly! Such a study is vitally important because what a person believes about his origin conditions what he believes about his future.

Both evolution and creation should be taught in the schools, but not as scientifically proven facts. Both should be presented as two possible explanations of our existence.

What should be emphasized is the evidence behind each proposal. One, special creation, is based upon the assumption of a Divine Creator while the other, evolution, is based upon the assumption of a naturalistic process without the aid of any supernatural being. The student would then be free to study the observable, measurable evidence that is offered as support for either theory. This would allow for maximum academic and personal freedom. Each student would have the right to draw his or her own conclusion based upon the evidence presented.

Such an approach is desirable for several reasons. Teaching both theories would be consistent with the academic freedom our educational system is built upon. Presenting both sides of an issue would produce a more profitable learning experience for students. To present only one side is to deny this learning opportunity. Dr. Richard Bliss, in *Acts and Facts*, June, 1978, offered evidence that students who had been presented both creation and evolution not only learned about the evidence supporting creation, but also produced test scores showing they had gained a greater understanding of evolution than did students in a control group where only evolution was taught.

Public school officials have shied away from presenting creation for fear of public criticism. Yet actual surveys do not support these fears. Thirteen hundred randomly surveyed homes in the Del Norte County School District in California showed 89 percent of the adults actually prefer that creation be taught in the public schools. A similar survey in the Cupertino Union School District (California) of almost 2000 homes showed 84 percent of the adults prefer creation be presented along with evolution.

A separate survey conducted by the Institute for Creation Research Midwest Center revealed that five percent of the adults felt that only evolution should be taught, 19 percent felt that only creation should be taught, and 64 percent felt that both creation and evolution should be presented. While the data produced by these surveys are limited, they provide a good indication of what adults believe to be fair in the public schools.

2. THE SEARCH FOR TRUTH

The most significant breakthrough in science was the development of the scientific method of inquiry. Conclusions would be reached only after a careful investigation of all possible evidence. No longer would the opinion of "highly respected persons" be the basis for scientific conclusions; theories must be proved through observation and experimentation. But this method of inquiry and problem solving did not happen overnight.

It would be virtually impossible to put a date on when men began to use the methods of empirical science to verify their hypotheses. However, it may safely be said that the birth, or rebirth, of inquiry began sometime within the fourteenth century when men became aware of the world around them through travel, for travel brought home strange and sometimes unbelievable stories of distant places. Curiosity thus led to inquiry: "I must see for myself." At the same time, men began to look more closely at the things immediately around them.

Without doubt, the greatest representative of the Renaissance was da Vinci Leonardo da Vinci, who excelled not only in almost every kind of art, but also as an engineer and inventor, as an anatomist and as an observer of nature. Leonardo began to compare the structure of man with that of animals, and he reached many illuminating conclusions. He accurately showed the relation of the bones in the human leg to those in the leg of a horse. He described the action of the eye, particularly in relation to lenses, and he made striking embryological observations. His investigation into the flight of birds may be said to be the start of scientific study of the mechanics of flight. Leonardo's greatness was not only due to his exceptional natural abilities, but also to his careful personal research based upon careful observations.

William Harvey (1578–1657), who mastered the idea of the circulatory system, was the first to give an adequate explanation of the body processes. His work was the starting point of the modern science of physiology and initiated the modern period of biology. His work, like that of Leonardo's, was based on careful experimentation and observation.

Men of science were becoming distinguished from other learned men by the very process in which they operated. First, the careful choosing of facts based upon observation; second, the formation of an hypothesis that linked the facts together; and third, the testing of the validity of the hypothesis. Rene Descartes, a contemporary of William Harvey and generally regarded as the founder of modern philosophy, resolved to "never accept anything as true which I do not clearly know to be such. . . ."

More and more, men were beginning to employ the inductive philosophy of inquiry, careful observations and conclusions based on the results of experimentation. Science thus became a precise branch of knowledge characterized by:

1. Demonstrated truths
2. Observed facts
3. Truths and facts logically related to other observed truths and facts.

But the development of this scientific method did not go without some uphill struggle. The problem was, and still is, that scientists are a unique group of people. They are devoted to their work but sometimes become easily "married," so to speak, to false hypotheses. Separation is not an easy task, even in the light of contrary evidence. Galileo, Pasteur, Lister, Copernicus and many others who made significant scientific discoveries faced the ridicule of fellow scientists who were unable to accept the new discoveries. It is obvious that scientists can be as biased as anyone, and new evidence is not always welcomed in scientific circles.

Theory of Evolution—How it Developed

Many people are convinced that Darwin (1809–1882) was the single person responsible for the development of the theory of evolution, but such simply isn't the case. Nevertheless, there is no name more closely associated with evolution than that of Charles Darwin. Before consideration is given to his role in evolution, a brief history of the development of the theory is necessary.

The ancient Greeks had some idea of evolution, although not in the formal sense of the theory of organic evolution as it is used today. Empedocles (490–430 BC) taught that parts of animals and men arose at random from the elements and were drawn together into various combinations, some of which were able to survive and propagate. Aristotle (384–322 BC) observed that organisms could be classified on a scale from the most simple to the most complex and inferred that creation must involve a perfecting principle responsible for this gradation. Francis Bacon (1561–1626) thought that some species of plants had arisen from others by degeneration, a kind of evolution in reverse.

But it was not until Comte de Buffon (1701–1788) that a real effort was made to document a naturalistic origin of life. Buffon paid little attention to the minute differences between species that the systematists were seeking but spent most of his time looking at the common factors or the likenesses. For Buffon, all parts and all activities of the world were interrelated. He questioned fixity of species, noting that animals have parts to which no special or adequate use could be described. This led to the theory of *vestigial organs*—those organs no longer considered to have any functional purpose. At one time this theory was used as conclusive proof that evolution had taken place. Today, however, few scientists hold to the vestigial theory. At one time evolutionists claimed there were about 180 vestigial organs in man. Some of these "useless" organs were the thyroid gland, the thymus, the coccyx, the pineal gland, the tonsils, and the appendix—all of which are now known to have useful, often essential, functions.

Buffon sought to trace the history of the earth through a series of "epochs," using fossils to provide a key to this history. He finally concluded that some species are degenerate forms of others; i.e., the ape is a degraded man, the donkey is a degraded horse and so on.

Erasmus Darwin (1731–1802), British botanist and grandfather of Charles Darwin, was the first to state the theory of "inheritance of acquired traits." Not aware of the genetic basis for heredity, he held that the changes species undergo in the course of time are due to factors outside the organism. These factors are able to influence the organism, causing changes that are then passed on to the offspring.

Jean Baptiste de Monet Lamarck (1744–1829) published his *Philosophie Zoologique* in 1809, the year of Charles Darwin's birth. Lamarck maintained that organic evolution is the universal principle of all nature. Although he was considered personally eccentric, Lamarck did make important and lasting contributions as a systematist. He separated spiders and crustaceans from insects and defined all these classes. He also introduced the classification of animals into vertebrates and invertebrates. However, his proneness to speculation often made him a laughing stock, and his scientific advancements often were not given serious consideration. He was opposed by Baron de Cuvier, whose recognized authority made his work unpopular for a time and delayed wide acceptance of the general theory of evolution. Charles Darwin, among his successors, held him in contempt.

Lamarck held that all life forms have a common ancestor and that all life forms are in constant change. The idea of the continuity of living things led Lamarck to consider that the animal and the plant species at some point in time must have been continuous with each other. For this study, he invented the term *biology*. He also proclaimed the "law of use and disuse" as the means for the mechanism of progressive development. For example, a deer-like animal, finding herbage scant, took to feeding on leaves of trees. It needed a longer neck to reach the leaves. In the course of time, the long neck became a more accentuated feature of the creature's anatomy and was passed on to its offspring. Thus emerged the giraffe.

Herbert Spencer (1820–1903) set forth the doctrine of evolution in 1852, seven years before Charles Darwin's *Origin of Species*. He began to use the word *evolution* for the first time to describe the process of production of higher from lower life forms. Charles Lyell had actually used the word some 20 years earlier, though in a less general sense. Spencer also coined the phrase *survival of the fittest* which gained rapid acceptance.

Darwin did not develop the theory of evolution—he seldom even used the word "evolution." However, through his efforts evolution became the popularly accepted theory that it is today.

Darwin had earlier rejected an opportunity to follow his father's footsteps and become a physician. He chose to become a clergyman instead. Still, he was not satisfied and eventually turned to his real love—the study of nature. His first break came in 1832 when he was offered a position as an unpaid naturalist on the surveying ship, *H.M.S. Beagle*. During its five-year scientific voyage, Darwin completed a set of notes that eventually led to the writing of the *Origin of Species by Means of Natural Selection*, published in 1859. Through this work, Darwin persuaded the scientific world that many diverse organic forms are of common descent, and that species are constantly changing and in some cases are even impossible to define.

Darwin was greatly influenced by a book written by Thomas Malthus on food consumption and human population. This book caused Darwin to discard his belief in special creation as the explanation of the origin of all living things. Up to the time that Darwin lived, many schools of theology had taught that there was a fixity of species which did not allow for any variation. On the voyage of the *Beagle*, Darwin was able to observe great variation within many species. As a result, he replaced his belief in special creation with a belief that competitive interactions of many varieties of living things in natural environments resulted over great lengths of time in changes within organisms. Some organisms became extinct while others produced new varieties that presumably became new kinds of organisms. Variation in organisms came about as a result of what Darwin called "natural selection." Nature, he believed, would always select those species best able to survive and allow them to propagate. Any variation beneficial to the organism would naturally cause its survival by means of natural selection.

Julian Huxley, one of the greatest supporters of Darwinian evolution, believed that Darwin's greatest contribution was that he provided a means, natural selection, for the elimination of the belief in special creation. But did Darwin actually provide the quantitative proof necessary to make this kind of claim? Not all who have studied Darwin's *Origin of Species* have drawn this conclusion. Dr. W.R. Thompson, a world-famous biologist, says in the introduction to Darwin's *Origin of Species* that Darwin had failed to produce sufficient paleontological evidence to prove his views. He stated that the evidence Darwin did produce was adverse to them.[1]

Darwin provided a mechanism, natural selection, through which most evolutionists believed change could be passed on to the offspring that would result in a constant improvement of a given species and eventual change into an entirely different species. However, actual observation shows that natural selection tends to eliminate misfits and preserve the stability of the species.

Natural selection explains that a given species survived because it was the most fit. But how do we know what species were the most fit? Simply because they survived? Natural selection has ended up explaining nothing.

what Darwin attempted to theorize, "explained nothing"

3. THE ORIGIN OF THE UNIVERSE— THEORIES AND PROBLEMS

I seriously doubt that there is a single person who has not at some time looked up into the night's starry sky and wondered about the purpose of it all. How did all those stars come to be? Who or what put them there? How many are there? How far away are they?

With the invention of the telescope it was learned that beyond the stars visible to the naked eye there were more stars. As telescopes became larger and more efficient, it was discovered that there is no apparent end to the stars of the universe. The further these telescopes reach, the more stars there seem to be.

The science of astronomy has taught us that stars occur in clusters called galaxies. The galaxy in which our solar system, the sun and the nine planets, is located is called the Milky Way galaxy. Estimates are that there may be as many as 100 billion stars within the Milky Way galaxy. Our sun is just one of those stars. Beyond the Milky Way galaxy are more galaxies, each composed of billions of stars. And like snowflakes, throughout the universe, no two galaxies are exactly alike. Each has its own uniqueness and each has its own orderliness.

These star systems do not speak of chaos but of orderliness. For the creationist they speak of the careful planning of a Divine Being. It is the handiwork of God. But for the evolutionist the universe speaks only of perplexity and unanswered questions. How could all this just have happened without a cause, a purpose, a designer? Rather than finding answers, cosmic evolutionists have only managed to provide more questions.

Out of Dust Comes Order?

In 1796, Marquis de LaPlace suggested that the universe came

19

THE MILKY WAY GALAXY

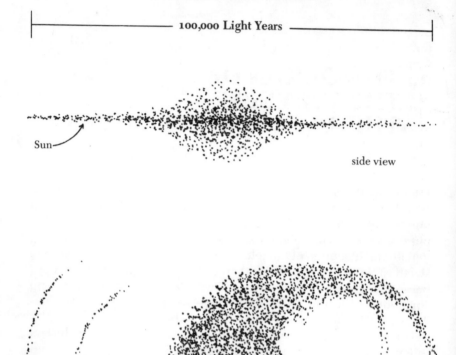

100,000 Light Years

Sun

side view

top view

So large is the Milky Way galaxy that it would take a person traveling at the speed of light, 186,000 miles per second, 100,000 years to travel from one end to the other. The nearest galaxy to the Milky Way, the Andromeda galaxy, is over two million light years away.

into being as the result of a very hot, rapidly rotating disk of gas that eventually cooled and condensed, thereby forming the sun. The planets resulted when gaseous rings were detached by centrifugal force from the main body of the sun during the early stages of its formation. LaPlace's theory came to be called the *nebular hypothesis*, better known as the *dust-cloud theory*. Most scientists eventually rejected the dust-cloud theory because it could not explain how gaseous rings could condense into planets. But practically every cosmic evolutionary theory presented since LaPlace's has the elements of the dust-cloud theory within it.

Serious thinking about the origin of the universe did not begin again until around the late 1920s when astronomers discovered that the universe is rapidly expanding. Primarily due to the work of the late Russian-born astrophysicist, George Gamow, the *big-bang theory* became the most generally accepted model for explaining the origin of the universe. Stated very simply, the big-bang theory suggests that the universe had its beginnings around 10,000 million years ago as a massive primordial cloud. All the matter known in the universe today had its origin in this cloud. For some unexplained reason, the cloud exploded, flinging all its substance into the outermost regions of the universe. Eventually, all the matter from this primordial cloud somehow managed to form the stars, planets and other cosmic members we know of today. Although Gamow's theory is more popular than LaPlace's, one should be able to see the similarity between the two. Gamow's theory is really only a modification of LaPlace's nebular hypothesis and must also deal with the same question: How could order arise from disorder?

The *steady-state theory* was developed as an alternative to Gamow's explanation of the origin of the universe. Briefly, the steady-state theory suggests that there is no need for an initial creative act because we are living in an eternal, never-ending universe that has always been and will always be. Somehow new matter is continually being created, *ex-nihilo*, throughout the universe. However, there is absolutely no evidence to support such an hypothesis.

A fourth concept, the *oscillating-universe theory*, attempts to combine the big-bang and the steady-state theories. Like the steady-state theory, this concept suggests that the universe has always been here. But at a given point in time, all the matter in the universe began to collapse inward to form the giant cloud of the big-bang theory. Once formed, the cloud exploded, sending all its substance outwards to form, once again, the universe. Those who hold to the oscillating-universe theory suggest that we are presently witnessing the outward movement of the most recent explosion that occurred some 10 billion years ago. It is the suggestion of these theorists that the universe has eternally oscillated between expansion and contraction states. But as is the case with the other theories, there isn't the slightest bit of evidence to support this hypothesis.

A fifth concept, the *planetesimal theory*, deals only with the origin of the planets and gives no clues to the origin of the sun. This theory was advanced by such men as Buffon, Sir James Jeans and others. According to their hypothesis, ages ago a large star came near enough to the sun to pull from its surface large tidal waves of hot gases that followed the whirling motions of the sun and eventually developed into the nine planets of the solar system. The large star continued on its voyage through space. What at first seemed to be a fairly reasonable theory has now turned into a very questionable hypothesis.

In the first place the planetesimal theory cannot give adequate explanation as to why the planets are so far from the sun. If this theory were true, all the planets would be closer to the sun than even the earth's orbit. Second, the tidal waves of gases would have been so hot they would have immediately dissipated into space. There would have been no chance of their forming into liquid or solid states.

Perhaps the most common characteristic of any theory of the origin of the universe is that for every theory advanced, another scientist seems to be able to produce scientific reasons as to why that theory cannot be true. But the cosmic evolutionist believes that these are the only alternatives possible.

"In the Beginning, God . . . "

Of course, there is another explanation for the origin of the universe: "In the beginning God created the heaven and the earth. . . ." I realize that many will immediately reject this theory because it has to do with "religion" whereas the others somehow manage to lie within the realm of science. While it is true that there are no known ways in which we can prove the Genesis account of the origin of the universe, neither can the cosmic evolutionists prove any of the evolutionary theories. But only the Genesis account is consistent with the universally accepted law of cause and effect: there is nothing that happens unless it has a cause. "In the beginning God . . . " becomes the cause of the origin of the universe. I am not aware of any evolutionary theory that can account for a cause.

There are many highly educated people who accept the Genesis account as the only logical explanation for the origin of the heavens. Many of these people have science backgrounds, and after a careful study of the evidence contrary to evolution they have chosen to reject evolution as a scientific theory.

As already explained, concepts that are not capable of observation, experimentation, or measurement lie outside the realm of empirical science. No one observed the origin of the earth, and there is no way in which to test the validity of the various cosmic theories. Therefore all theories dealing with origins lie within the realm of "religion" because they cannot be proved. They must be accepted by faith.

The non-Biblical theories are plagued with serious problems and in many cases are in actual violation of known physical laws. Any scientist desiring to present an unbiased account of the origin of the universe should list the faults within his proposed theory, but this is seldom done. Often a favorite theory is presented in such a way as to lead the reader to believe that the theory is substantiated by factual evidence when the fact is that no such evidence exists. Consider just a few of the problems that cosmic evolutionists have failed to deal with in their various theories.

Problem One: Obtaining Order

The big-bang, steady-state and oscillating-universe theories are really no more than modifications of the original nebular hypothesis of LaPlace's. All have failed to account for how random, primary particles—mainly hydrogen—came to exist and then managed to collect into the various star clusters, or galaxies, with all their individual star members. It doesn't matter which of these theories is being considered; the problem is basically the same: How could the random particles of a proposed gigantic dust-cloud become so highly organized as is the universe today? The only observable processes at work today are not building complexity out of random particles but rather are going the other direction—toward decay and breakdown.

All leading scientists tell us that the universe is not getting more organized but is becoming more disorganized and will eventually end up as a cold and dark collection of dead stars and cosmic dust. This is certainly consistent with what is known about the second law of thermodynamics, which states that any organized system will move, in time, into a state of disorganization.

Issac Asimov, in "In the Game of Energy and Thermodynamics You Can't Even Break Even" (see *Smithsonian Institute Journal,* June, 1970), describes the second law as another way of saying the entire universe is getting more disorderly. Even a room, if left alone, will soon become dusty and musty. It makes no difference whether we are discussing star systems, houses, machinery or our bodies. *All* will eventually deteriorate, collapse, break down, wear out. It is because of the second law that so much energy must be spent in mending, repainting, repairing, and replacing. We can only temporarily overcome the effects of the second law; it will have its way in the end.

Proponents of evolutionary theories suggesting a random dust-cloud that eventually became the highly ordered universe we observe today must explain how this could have happened in light of the second law of thermodynamics. Organization is not the result of random movement of building particles. In other words, an explosion in a brickyard will not produce buildings!

Dr. Henry Morris of the Institute for Creation Research in San Diego, California, finds it incredible that many intelligent people actually believe that order came from chaos as suggested by evolutionists.

> One of the strangest phenomena of human nature is that brilliant minds often make foolish decisions. There is no more common and universal fact of experience than the fact that order never arises spontaneously out of disorder and a design always requires a designer. Yet many scientists and other intellectuals believe that our intricately-designed and infinitely-ordered universe developed by itself out of primeval chaos![1]

There are some who suggest that the energy of the original explosion—the Big-Bang—might have provided the necessary energy to redirect the tendency for randomness toward complexity. This explanation is not supported by evidence, however. Any person who has witnessed the result of an explosion has seen what unharnessed energy produces—chaos! Raw energy by itself does not increase complexity. In order for complexity to arise from disorder, there must be some kind of control to direct and guide the energy. A bull in a department store would represent a tremendous amount of energy, but organization would not be the end result. One simply must have energy that is directed and controlled if complexity is to be the result.

Problem Two: Getting it all Together

Dr. Gerard P. Kuiper, a noted American astronomer and director of the McDonald Observatory in Mt. Locke, Texas, has indicated that the dust-cloud theorists are still nowhere near solving the problem that caused the rejection of LaPlace's hypothesis: How did the primary particles manage to come together to form the stars and planets? Some have suggested that gravitational attraction was sufficient to pull the particles together. Dr. Kuiper believes that before gravitational attraction could become significant, the assumed primordial particles would have to be as big as the moon! But cosmic evolutionists are suggesting that this happened with particles no larger than atoms.

Problem Three: Out of Nothing?

Perhaps the most elementary problem facing any person wishing to study origins is the question of how it all came into being in the first place. What was the source of the dust-cloud or the primary particles that made up the dust-cloud? Where did they come from? In light of the law of cause and effect, these are perfectly legitimate questions. Nothing happens except that it has a cause.

Hydrogen, the most abundant material in the universe, is continually being fused into the more complex element of helium within the star systems of the universe. This means that when all the hydrogen is used up, the stars that do not become novae (exploding stars) will "burn out," and the universe will become filled with cold, dwarf stars capable of producing neither heat nor light. Everything will end up in a dark, cold, dead universe.

To avoid the concept of being faced with a dying universe, which would imply that the universe must also have had a beginning, some have suggested that the universe is alternately expanding and contracting—the Oscillating-Universe theory. This suggests that the presently expanded universe will stop its outward movement and begin moving back to the place of its origin. But what force is there that has the ability to reach billions of light years in all directions in the universe and still have enough power to attract the distant galaxies and pull them all together? No such force is known to exist. One scientist suggested that at a certain point in time, time itself will begin to run backwards, and this will be the force capable of causing the entire universe to contract and return to the place of its origin. There is, of course, absolutely no scientific basis for this belief.

Estimates show that at the present rate of expansion, it would take only 10 billion years to empty the heaven of all the galaxies we now observe. If the dust-cloud explosion took place 10 billion years ago as suggested by cosmic evolutionists, we should not be able to observe any galaxy. Yet, we can see other galaxies. The Andromeda galaxy can even be seen by trained eyes without the aid of a telescope.

This "thinning out of the universe" has caused a few scientists to adopt the highly speculative theory of *continuous creation*, otherwise known as the steady-state theory. It suggests that matter is in the process of being continually created throughout the universe. Where does the matter come from? According to this theory, it simply appears—it is created out of nothing and by nothing! At one time the particles comprising the substance of the universe do not exist and at a later time they do. This is creation *without* a creator, and is most certainly in violation of the law of cause and effect as well as the first law of thermodynamics. This latter law, also known as the *law of conservation of matter and energy*, states that neither matter nor energy is being created today.

Energy may appear in a variety of forms: heat, mechanical, chemical, electrical and so forth. While energy may be able to change from one form to another, it *cannot* change its quantity. This is the essence of the first law of thermodynamics. It is now known that matter is also a form of energy, but this fact does not alter the basic principle of the first law.

According to this basic and well-established scientific law, *there is nothing which is being created or destroyed.* Energy is defined as that property which measures the capacity of doing work. Everything in the universe is subject to this basic law. There are no known exceptions. It is consistent with the special creation account in

Genesis which states that the Divine Creator completed His work of creation in six days and rested on the seventh. There are no creative processes occurring today. Evolutionists who adhere to the speculative theory of continuous creation must ignore the first law of thermodynamics.

The present processes of nature are not processes of creation and integration but rather of conservation and disintegration. The available energy in the observable universe is continually changing into a lower grade of energy that is not sufficiently strong enough to do work. The universe is dying—it is running out of usable energy. It is growing old!

Problem Four: Dust to Stars?

Assuming that the particles of the universe did come together to form large whirling spheres of gas that eventually collected into the stars and the planets, the evolutionists are now faced with a fourth major problem. How did the small eddies (vortices) of gas remain intact during the period of planetary accretion or formation? Dr. Kuiper finds this a most perplexing problem:

> It is difficult to conceive that the beautiful system of vortices could actually have been in existence long enough—even 10 or 100 years—to get the condensation of the building material for the planets under way.[2]

No adequate explanation of this serious problem has been made. Maybe at this point a new theory should be developed that would be called the *somehow theory*. It could be used each time a problem faced the cosmic evolutionists and would simply state that *somehow* it all happened anyway.

Problem Five: Something Left Behind

The fifth problem is no less a problem than the four already mentioned. Assuming that the sun did form from a gigantic whirling sphere of cosmic dust, the question is, What caused the process to stop so that the entire mass of the system did not form one large body? The sun makes up 99.9 percent of the mass of the solar system.

What prevented a meager 00.1 percent from also falling into the main body?

Problem Six: The Slow Sun

A sixth problem can be likened to an ice-skater about to perform a pirouette. With arms extended, the skater slowly begins to twirl. But notice what happens to the speed at the center of the pirouette as the skater begins to draw the arms in closer to the body. The pirouette becomes so rapid that we only see a blur. This spinning speed of the skater is known as *angular momentum.*

Considering the immense vastness of the dust-cloud that had to collect in order to form the sun, the angular momentum of the central figure, the sun, must be unbelievably rapid. This is not what is observed, however. A leading university astronomer calculated that if the sun were formed from a condensing, spiralling mass of gas as proposed by the dust-cloud theory, the final angular momentum of the central object would be an impossible billion times faster than the rotation speed actually observed of the sun. The problem now facing cosmic evolutionists is to explain where or how the sun managed to expend all but one ten-millionth of one percent of its original angular momentum.

The sun contains over 99 percent of all the matter in the entire solar system and yet possesses only a mere 2 percent of the system's total angular momentum. However, the lightweight planets contain less than one percent of the solar system's matter but possess a staggering 98 percent of its angular momentum! Builders of model solar systems who cannot offer an adequate explanation for an anomaly in the evolutionary theory of the solar system such as this should not proceed any further.

I once mentioned this problem to a science educator who simply responded "I'm not concerned with problems like that because I'm certain the scientists know what they are doing." No wonder this person remains an evolutionist to this very day—he is not willing to consider any evidence that opposes evolution.

The planet Jupiter possesses the greatest angular momentum in the solar system. Why is this so? It shouldn't be, according to the. dust-cloud theories. Furthermore, if the sun managed to get rid of practically all of its angular momentum, why have not the planets done likewise?

Problem Seven: Too Much Tilt!

Problem number seven is concerned with the eccentric and inclined orbits observed in the solar system. All the planets move in the same direction around the sun: counterclockwise when viewed from the North Star. All nine planets have nearly circular orbits, and all nine planets have orbits in almost the same plane, which is approximately the plane of the sun's equator. This is exactly what is expected by the cosmic evolutionists and their various dust-cloud theories on the origin of the solar system.

However, considerable variation does occur among the members of the solar system. Of the planets, Mercury (smallest and closest to the sun) and Pluto (outermost planet) have the most eccentric and highly inclined orbits with inclinations of 7 degrees and 17 degrees respectively and eccentricities of 24 percent and 20 percent respectively. This is not to be expected, nor has an adequate explanation been given for this irregularity. The asteroid belt has still higher eccentricities and inclinations. Comets and meteors show little trace whatever of the two expected regularities.

Such variation from the expected casts a long shadow of doubt on any dust-cloud theory. But Mercury and Pluto are not the only planets that demonstrate deviations from the expected.

Problem Eight: Venus and Uranus

If all the planets were formed from eddies of gas spun off the early-forming sun by centrifugal force, the very last characteristic to be expected would be a solar member with a retrograde (reverse) rotation in relation to the other solar members. But such is the case with two members of the system, Uranus and Venus. These two planets rotate on their axes in the opposite direction of the other seven planets. In addition, the axis of Uranus deviates by 98 percent and yet its orbit is less inclined than that of any other planet. W. M. Smart, professor of astronomy at the University of Glasgow, admits that these variations pose serious problems for the present evolutionary theories on the origin of the solar system:

> It must be confessed that it is difficult to account for the exceptional circumstances relating to Uranus if we regard, as indeed we do, the uniformities of orbital and rotational motion in gen-

eral as providing an incontrovertible argument in favor of the common origin of thè planetary system.[3]

Venus has yet another peculiarity; it not only rotates, like Uranus, in an opposite direction, but also has a rotation rate of only one revolution every 240 days. In comparison, the earth rotates once every 24 hours, and Jupiter, largest planet in the system, rotates once every ten hours.

Problem Nine: Wrong-Way Moons

Of the 31 known satellites (moons) in the solar system, 11 demonstrate retrograde behaviors. They revolve around their primaries in a direction contrary to that in which all other planets and satellites revolve. If these moons are, as proposed by evolutionary theories, fragments of their respective "mother" planets, then they should revolve in the same direction. Such a large percentage of retrograde revolutions cannot be explained away as minor exceptions to the rule. Celestial mechanics cannot explain why such variation exists.

This means that 13 members of the solar system (planets and satellites) demonstrate major deviations from the proposed expectations of the theory of cosmic evolution. When 32.5 percent of the solar members become exceptions to the rule, there is a definite problem. I believe, however, that such variation is exactly what would be expected to occur as a result of special creation.

In accordance with the evolutionary theories, the primary body, the planet, must always carry the bulk of the angular momentum in relation to the associated satellites. Yet studies reveal that this is not true of the earth-moon system where the moon carries the bulk of the angular momentum. How have the evolutionary theorists explained this? No adequate explanation has yet been provided.

Problem Ten: Origin of the Moon

An even more perplexing problem arises concerning the earth-moon relationship. The chemical composition of rock and soil in the vicinity of the Apollo Eleven landing site in the Sea of Tranquility was unlike any known part of Earth. This finding has led many scientists to hypothesize that the earth and its moon may have had entirely different origins. The lunar samples brought back to the earth contain surprisingly large amounts of such rare earth elements as chromium, titanium, yttrium, and zirconium. Crystalline igneous rocks were found to have as much as 12 percent titanium oxide, whereas the richest lodes on Earth have no more than 4.5 percent.

It is now known that the moon has an average density a full third less than the density of Earth. If both bodies were formed of much the same materials at about the same time and by the same process, then what can account for this discrepancy in composition and density?

The moon is receding from the earth at a rate of about five inches per year. This discovery was made in the late 1890s by George Darwin, a noted British astronomer and son of Charles Darwin. This observation is what caused George Gamow to extrapolate that the moon was pulled out of the earth about 4 billion years ago. He believed that the Pacific Basin is the result of the scar that marks the point of the moon's departure. At one time this was a very promising theory, but it is now rejected by most leading scientists. Evolutionists, however, still insist that the earth is 4 to 5 billion years old. Though the theory has proved to be invalid, the age is still important. An immensity of time is very important to the various evolutionary theories and may be the reason why evolutionists are reluctant to give up the age aspect of Gamow's theory.

Though many theories have been proposed, astronomers must admit that they are completely at a loss as to the origin of the satellite systems. If the earth and moon were formed from a single source, not only would they have similar compositions and density, but it would also have been necessary for the original mass to have a rotational period of approximately four hours. Certainly such a mass would tend to break up and possibly form two rotating bodies. But the difference in composition and density between the two has caused most astronomers to look more favorably upon the proposal that the earth and the moon were originally formed as two separate bodies.

Problem Eleven: Origin of the Elements

There are only 92 naturally occurring elements, and apart from hydrogen and helium, all these elements are extremely rare throughout the universe. Elements beyond helium amount to only about one percent of the total mass of the sun. Therefore it seems very unlikely that the sun would be a suitable source for the formation of the planets whose compositions are quite unlike that of the sun. Furthermore, the interstellar gas throughout the universe appears to be made of the same basic material making up the sun and other stars. Just how did the heavier elements found on earth come to exist in the ratio in which they are found?

George Gamow proposed that our present universe started from an exceedingly dense core of protons and neutrons which exploded about ten billion years ago. Within seconds, all the elements known to exist were formed. The elements were believed to have been formed by a process known as *neutron capture*. But if this were true, the most complex element would have been no more complex than helium, according to Drs. Alpher and Herman.[4]

Where did the hydrogen and primary atomic particles come from in the first place? We know that all matter is subject to the laws of thermodynamics and in particular the second law, also known as the *law of entropy*. All systems, whether as large as a galaxy or as small as an atom, show a tendency to run out of usable energy; that is, to break down, wear out, decay, eventually to collapse. All systems show some degree of organization that is gradually becoming disorganized. There are no known exceptions. This is what any study of origins must concern itself with: How did complexity arise in the first place?

Fred Hoyle, a leading proponent of the steady-state theory, made an interesting stab at the problem. His answer, however, leaves much to be desired:

> I find myself forced to assume that the nature of the Universe requires continuous creation—the perpetual bringing into being background material. . . . Where does the created material come from? It appears not from anywhere. Material appears—it is created. At one time the various atoms composing the material do not exist, and at a later time they do . . . [5]

It is interesting that the special creation theory of Genesis must be rejected by the cosmic evolutionists because it cannot be proven, while the steady-state theory requires an even greater amount of faith. Matter is simply being created but without the aid of a creator. The law of cause and effect insists that nothing happens without a cause. But here we are told, and expected to believe, that out of nothing comes matter.

No matter which theory is proposed—LaPlace's, Gamow's, Hoyle's, or any other variation—they all fail to explain the origin of the observable universe with its magnificent orderliness and variation.

Problem Twelve: The Mysterious Comets

Comets are among the largest members of the solar system. The core of a comet may have a diameter of 10,000 miles or more, and the surrounding coma may have a diameter as large as 50,000 miles. The trailing tail may measure in the millions of miles in length. Yet the density of a comet is believed to be only a fraction of that of the earth.

Comets may be divided into two major groups: long-period and short-period. Short-period comets, such as the famous Halley's Comet, have solar periods around 100 years or less. Halley's Comet makes a complete revolution around the sun once every 75 years. Long-period comets may not return for hundreds or thousands of years.

Very little is known about the origin of comets. Their density is so small that they are believed to be made of various gases. These gases have been partially determined by spectrum analysis. They seem to come from beyond the orbit of Pluto. Some scientists think there may be something like a "deep-freeze" storage of comets about 14 billion miles from the sun.

Measurements suggest that a comet tends to lose about 1/200th of its substance with each trip around the sun. Extremely small particles are blown out of the solar system by solar radiation, whereas larger particles are pulled into the sun. A German astronomer has estimated that the very maximum life of a short-period comet would be only 25,000 years. Others have suggested that the estimate should be even less. Yet evolutionists believe that comets came into being with the other solar members, about 4.5 billion years ago. If this is true, some explanation must be given as to how a short-period comet with a period of only 100 years could have survived some 45 million trips around the sun. Even a long-period comet would have to overcome the same problem if given 4.5 billion years of existence. A comet with a period of 100,000 years would still have to survive some 45,000 solar trips.

Looking at the same problem from another direction, the severity of the problem becomes even more obvious. If a long-period comet with an average period of 100,000 years lost not just 1/200th of its substance, but only 1/1000th with each trip around the sun (this is a *very* conservative figure!), then some 4.5 billion years ago the original mass of that comet would have been some 10^{19} times its present mass, or several times the mass of the sun! This simply cannot be. Comets speak of a very young solar system.

Problem Thirteen: It's a Dusty Universe

Along with the mystery of the origin of comets and their decay rate is the problem of the tremendous amount of dust particles still within the solar system. Solar radiation would tend to exceed the force of gravity on particles of very small size—those with diameters of only a few angstroms. One angstrom (A°) is equal to 10^{-8} centimeters (1/100,000,000 cm). It is estimated that solar radiation would have pushed these particles out of the solar system in only two billion years. Larger particles would have been pulled into the sun. Particles less than three inches in diameter inside the orbit of the planet Jupiter would have been pulled into the sun in only two billion years. Yet according to Harold Slusher in an article entitled "The Age of the Solar System" (see *CREATION-Acts-Facts-Impacts*, edited by Henry Morris, ICR Publishing Company, San Diego, Calif., 1974), particles of this size appear to be in great abundance within interplanetary space. How can this be, unless the solar system is less than two billion years of age?

Cosmic dust in its movement toward the sun falls on the earth at an estimated rate of about 14,000,000 tons per year. In the proposed 4.5 billion years of the existence of the earth and the solar system, this would have amounted to a deposit of over 180 feet of cosmic or meteoric dust covering the entire earth.[6] Erosional processes would have washed or blown most of this dust into the oceans. Cosmic dust has been found to be very high in the element nickel; 2.5 percent or about a 300 times greater concentration than that which is found in the earth's crust. But, of course, because of the erosional processes at work, we would not expect to find a great amount of meteoric nickel on the solid part of the earth, the lithosphere. So we turn to the oceans in an effort to find the nickel of the cosmic dust—yet it is not to be found in sufficient quantities in the oceans. The extremely small amount of nickel in the oceans would have been formed in only 7,000 to 8,000 years, assuming it all came from cosmic dust.

Lunar samples were expected to provide a clue to the missing cosmic dust on the earth. Instead, the findings on the moon's surface only confirmed that which is found on the earth. The smaller diameter of the moon exerts a gravitational force only 1/6th that of the earth. Therefore, the amount of cosmic dust would not be expected to be nearly as much as what *should* have been found on the earth. Nevertheless, lunar probes were still expected to find several feet of meteoric dust covering the moon's surface. Reports from the first lunar landing site showed that little more than 1/8th of an inch of meteoric dust was on the surface of the moon (*El Paso Herald-Post*, July 21, 1969). It would take less than 10,000 years to accumulate this meager amount. Subsequent landings in lunar "seas" discovered larger dust accumulations, but still very small in thickness. Such findings do not lend support to the hypothesis that the moon is 4.5 billion years old.

I realize that the above problems with the evolutionary theory may be somewhat disturbing to many people who have been told that evolution is a certainty. But I am convinced that scientists have the obligation to present all known evidence, withholding none, even if it discredits a popular theory such as evolution.

4. CONDITIONS NECESSARY FOR LIFE

Life, defined simply as "a state of being," is one of the most perplexing properties known to man. To this date, it still lacks adequate definition. Like the concept of gravity, we can only tell what it does, not what it is. In teaching about "living" organisms, we explain that such organisms, animals and plants, possess certain characteristics that separate them from the *non*living world. Among these characteristics are reproduction, growth, metabolism, cellular structure, self-initiated movement and responses to stimuli. None of these, however, gives an adequate definition of what life really is. All that scientists have been able to do so far is to tell *about* the concept of life, while life itself continues to elude definition and thereby remains a major mystery.

As far as we know, the only place in the universe where living organisms may be found is the planet Earth. Some astronomers have estimated that there may be as many as 600 million planets in the Milky Way Galaxy capable of supporting carbon-based life. However, it should be noted that this is only speculation and not based on any observable evidence. If we are to limit our discussion of life to that which we actually know, then we must limit our discussion to the planet Earth. There are only nine known planets in the whole Milky Way galaxy! This is certainly not to say that there could be no more, but just a statement that we know of no other planets outside the nine in our own solar system.

The assumption that there may be 600 million "inhabited" planets in our galaxy is based upon another assumption: that since the sun, planets, and other members of the solar system were formed by the condensation of an assumed dust-cloud that existed at a time in the distant past, then this very process must have also taken place in other parts of the universe. Neither assumption is supported by evidence nor capable of being proved.

The earth seems to be uniquely suited for maintaining living organisms. It not only possesses just the right conditions necessary for life to exist, but also its size and distance from the sun seem to be perfect. I believe this is clear evidence that the earth was uniquely designed and positioned so that it could support life.

Scientists tell us that if there were just a 10 percent variation in the size of the earth, either an increase or decrease, life on Earth would be very unlikely. Should Earth have been positioned just a few million miles closer or further from the sun, again life would be jeopardized. Even the tilt of Earth's axis is significant. Should the axis have been perfectly perpendicular to the plane of the earth's orbital path, one-half of the land surface could not be cultivated or even likely inhabited.

The 24-hour rotation period of the earth is also perfectly suited to support life. If this period were longer or shorter, the existence of life would be doubtful. It seems that no other planet in the solar system possesses the life-giving qualities as those found on Earth. The odds are numerically against so many "right" conditions having been the result of some cosmic accident.

The Psalmist David exclaimed: "The heaven, even the heavens, are the Lord's; but the earth hath he given to the children of men." If this thought came by Divine revelation, and I believe it did, then it is probably safe to assume that no higher forms of life exist beyond the boundaries of the earth. While this thought presents no problem for the creationist, it may be somewhat difficult for the evolutionist to accept.

When various space probes failed to detect life on the planet Mars, the most likely planet outside the earth even remotely capable of supporting life, one prominent individual was quoted as having said: "I suddenly felt all alone in the universe." A British scientist concluded that if life as known on the earth is the only life that pretends to consciousness, then man can be nothing more than a freak, fashioned by the blind forces of chemical reactions, and "his lofty ideals, philosophies and religions are nothing but echoes of a singularly negative existence."

While the evolutionists may be somewhat disturbed by the thought of life not existing elsewhere in the universe, the creationists find this to be consistent with the Genesis account of creation.

Dr. Vance Oyama, one of the three Project Viking biologists and developer of the Viking's gas exchange experiment, has concluded that Mars may be unable to support life.[1] Dr. Oyama holds that huge quantities of oxygen present on the red planet have formed unstable oxygen compounds such as ozone, peroxides and superoxides. These compounds, he argues, would not allow organic compounds to form or even to persist if they did manage to develop. This may explain why Viking's organic chemistry instruments have been unable to detect organic materials on Mars. Dr. Oyama points out that all the gas changes occurring in the Viking experiments "can most easily be explained or demonstrated by plausible chemical reactions that require no biological processes" (see "The Viking Gas Exchange Experiment Results from Chryse and Utopia Surface Samples", by V. I. Oyama and B. J. Berdahl in *Journal of Geophysical Research*, Vol. 82, No. 28, September 30, 1977).

Many scientists, however, believe it may be possible that less complex life forms such as anaerobic bacteria, photosynthetic blue-green algae or lichens may exist in eco-niches that are protected from ultraviolet rays and other harmful conditions known to exist on Mars. If organisms are hiding in sheltered niches such as under or within a rock, then admittedly the detection of these inaccessible life forms would be very difficult. However, for every living microbe, there should be the remains of thousands of dead ones that could easily be detected.

Viking Two's soil organic detector failed to find organic compounds in the Martian soil—even when the lander arm pushed aside a rock and dug a soil sample that had not been exposed to ultraviolet rays (see "Sifting for Life in the Sands of Mars", by Rick Gore in *National Geographic*, Vol. 151, No. 1, January, 1977). This is certainly not to say that simple life forms as those mentioned above do not exist on Mars, but that until organic compounds can be found in the soil, biologists should be reluctant to conclude that Mars has life.

Life, at least complex life forms, is capable of existence only under certain conditions such as a proper temperature range, an adequate supply of water in the liquid state, a properly balanced atmosphere, a solar energy conversion mechanism, and the presence of many organic and inorganic compounds. There are many other necessary conditions not mentioned here and, I am certain, even more conditions of which science is not presently aware. But it would be foolish to consider the origin of life without giving attention to the various conditions necessary for the existence of known life forms. A more careful look will be made of just the five essential conditions mentioned above.

Condition One: A Proper Temperature

Living organisms exist within a relatively small temperature range when compared to the temperature extremes that exist within the universe. Nearly every organism must exist within a range from approximately -50°F. to approximately 120°F.—a total range of 170°F. There are a few organisms that can tolerate temperatures beyond this range. *Chlorella*, a small variety of algae, can survive up to 185°F., and some bacteria have survived very cold storage for several years, but this is still narrow when one considers the extreme temperatures that are present outside the protective layers of the earth's atmosphere.

Mercury, the closest planet to the sun, has a surface temperature hot enough to melt lead. Temperatures on Venus are also too extreme to expect life forms to be found there. The 98 percent carbon dioxide atmosphere of Venus helps to maintain a relatively even atmospheric temperature on the surface at about 700°F.! Mars is the only planet outside the earth with a temperature range that falls within the limits necessary for life. Noontime temperatures may reach between 40°F. to 50°F., but fall to a -130°F. during the Martian nights.

Beyond Mars, the possibility of life forms existing is seldom seriously considered because of the extremely cold and hostile conditions believed to exist on the outer planets.

Condition Two: An Adequate Supply of Water

If the element carbon is most closely associated with life, then water must be the compound that is most closely associated with the living. Water is essential to life. Most living things are made up of approximately 70 percent water. Man is required to use no less than 4½ quarts of water daily to maintain proper health. The water must be available in liquid form.

Water has several chemical characteristics that make it important for other reasons as well:

1. Water's high heat-holding capacity serves as a natural insulator

against extreme changes in temperatures. When compared to other substances, a larger quantity of heat is required to bring an increase in the temperature of a given quantity of water. Just as a lake or ocean has a cooling effect on the environment during the summer and a warming effect during the winter, so our body fluids (mostly water) tend to have the same effect on our bodies. Water serves as a very effective thermostat for the body.

2. A tremendous amount of energy (500–600 calories per gram) is required to change the liquid state of water to vapor. Because vaporization of water removes large quantities of heat, perspiration is an effective cooling process in animals. Transpiration, the evaporation of water from leaves, brings the same result in plants. The upper limits of life are reached at about 104°F. for most organisms. Few plants and animals can be active and some cannot even live above this temperature. But both plants and animals are frequently exposed to conditions where the absorption of heat might easily raise their body temperatures above this critical level were it not for perspiration and transpiration.

3. A very unusual characteristic of water is that it reaches its greatest density slightly above freezing, around 39°F. Below this temperature, water begins to expand, increasing its volume by 1/12th. This means that ice is less dense than water and will float when placed in water. If it were not for this unique property that causes water to stop contracting at 39°F., it would become more dense, and lakes and ponds would freeze from the bottom up, killing all life in them.

4. Water vapor in the atmosphere tends not only to help filter out harmful solar radiations, but also provides a type of "greenhouse" effect that prevents the loss of long heat waves during the nights and reduces the temperature variation between the night and day. Perhaps you have already noticed that an overcast night is usually warmer than nights when the sky is cloudless and crystal clear.

5. Water is known as the universal solvent; that is, more substances will dissolve in water than in any other known liquid. Fortunately not all substances can dissolve in water or else there would not be a container capable of holding water. It is probable that all chemical reactions within living protoplasm take place between substances in solution or in colloidal suspensions involving water.

It is obvious that life is dependent upon water. Most organisms can loose nearly all their fat and still live, up to 50 percent of their protein and still continue to survive; but if an organism should loose only 20 percent of its body fluid, it is sure to die. Anyone seriously looking for life beyond our own planet must look for a place where there is an abundant supply of water—and in the liquid state.

Condition Three: An Atmosphere of Sufficient Density and Composition

Our atmosphere, which is comprised of 20 percent oxygen and has an atmospheric pressure of 14.7 lbs/in² at sea level, is also unique in the solar system. No other atmosphere is comparable to that of Earth's. The Martian atmosphere is only 1/100th the density of the earth's and is composed of 95 percent carbon dioxide. This rules out the possibility of any *complex* life forms existing there. Excess carbon dioxide in the atmosphere would be toxic to complex life forms. In space capsules, it is essential that excess carbon dioxide be removed from the capsule's atmosphere to prevent poisoning the astronauts.

Atmospheric pressure less than 5 lbs/in² would be insufficient to support very complex life forms. Atmospheric pressure on Mars is far below this critical limit. When we breath in air (inhale), the oxygen taken into the lungs must then pass through the thin membrane of the lungs and into the capillary blood vessels so that it can be carried to the various parts of the body. Without an adequate atmospheric pressure, oxygen could not pass through the thin membrane lining of the lungs. This is another critical condition that concerns astronauts and their survival.

Of course, an adequate supply of free oxygen must be available to animals and non-photosynthetic plants (those unable to manufacture food from sunlight) if they are to exist. Even photosynthetic plants depend on oxygen during the night when photosynthesis is not possible. These plants have to reverse the photosynthetic process at night when solar energy is no longer available and exhibit the respiration process commonly associated only with animals.

In addition, the density of the earth's atmosphere, with its various gases such as ozone and water vapor, helps protect living organisms from harmful solar radiations. The thin atmosphere of Mars is not capable of protecting its surface from ultraviolet radiations from the

COMPOSITION OF THE EARTH'S ATMOSPHERE

Stable constituents

ELEMENT OR COMPOUND	SYMBOL	PERCENTAGE
Nitrogen	N_2	78.084%
Oxygen	O_2	20.946%
Argon	A	.934%
Carbon dioxide	CO_2	.033%
Neon	Ne	*
Helium	He	*
Methane	CH_4	*
Krypton	Kr	*
Hydrogen	H_2	*
Nitrous oxide	N_2O	*
Xenon	Xe	*

*Extremely small amount.

Variable constituents

ELEMENT OR COMPOUND	SYMBOL
Water vapor	H_2O
Hydrogen peroxide	H_2O_2
Ozone	O_3
Ammonia	NH_3
Hydrogen sulfide	H_2S
Sulphur dioxide	SO_2
Sulphur trioxide	SO_3
Radon	RaEm
Dust	–

sun. Earth's ozone layer begins about nine miles up and reaches its maximum at about 14 miles. It shields the earth's surface against lethal ultraviolet radiation from the sun.

Without the protective layer of ozone in the upper atmosphere, radiation from the sun would soon render the earth's surface incapable of supporting life.

Dr. R. A. Deering, professor of physics at New Mexico Highlands University, provides evidence that suggests ultraviolet irradiation can alter the genetic structure of the cell, deoxyribonucleic acid (DNA)—particularly radiation of wavelengths of 2,600 angstroms, which seem to be the most destructive.[2] This has been substantiated by laboratory experiments using monochromatic ultraviolet radiations at different wavelengths.

Biologists are particularly concerned with wavelengths between 2,000 and 3,000 angstroms, because within this range DNA absorbs ultraviolet radiation very rapidly.

The dangerous effects of ultraviolet radiation have been known since the discovery in 1877 that it can kill bacteria. It is known that ultraviolet radiation can delay cell division and prevent cells from synthesizing certain essential substances. It can also alter the semipermeability of the cell's membrane, affecting the way in which substances enter and leave the cell. It is capable of producing abnormalities in chromosomes that are responsible for producing harmful mutations.

I believe that it is by design, not chance, that the earth's ozone layer absorbs most of the ultraviolet radiation that is so destructive to living cells. It is too carefully designed and balanced to be a perchance formation.

Condition Four: An Energy Conversion Mechanism

An adequate source of energy is essential to the existence of life, but the energy must be in a useable form. Our planet is an open system and receives a tremendous amount of energy from the sun every second of every hour of every day. However, before energy is capable of doing work, two conditions must be present: first, a mechanism capable of converting the energy into a useable energy form, and second, another mechanism that is capable of directing the use of this converted energy.

> ... the simple expenditure of energy is not sufficient to develop and maintain order. A bull in a china shop performs work, but he neither creates nor maintains organization. The work needed is particular work; it must follow specification; it requires information on how to proceed.[3]

The only organisms capable of converting and storing the energy from the sun are green plants, those with the ability to perform the process of photosynthesis. This very complex biological process con-

Ultraviolet Absorption Spectrum of DNA

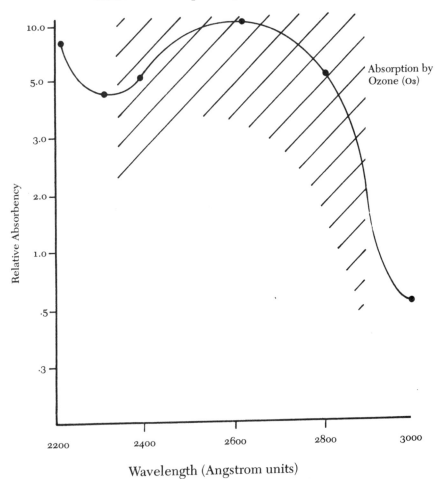

Wavelength (Angstrom units)

Dr. R. A. Deering determined that DNA is the most sensitive to ultraviolet wavelengths of 2600 A°. Ozone in the upper atmosphere absorbs most of the ultraviolet radiation between 2000 and 3000 A°.

verts water and carbon dioxide from the atmosphere in the presence of sunlight into sugar and oxygen. All life is ultimately dependent on this process.

Photosynthesis

$$CO_2 + H_2O \xrightarrow{\text{in the presence of:}} C_6H_{12}O_6 + O_2$$

(carbon dioxide)   (water)   1. sunlight   (sugar)   (oxygen)
2. chlorophyll

Something must control the process of photosynthesis. The very complex DNA, which makes up the genetic units of the cell, maintains the development and organization of the chloroplasts that make photosynthesis possible.

These mechanisms—the energy-conversion mechanism of the chloroplasts and the energy-directing mechanism of the DNA—must be present at the same time.

Condition Five: The Presence of Many Organic and Inorganic Compounds

A very large number of organic and inorganic compounds must be readily available if life is to exist. The DNA that controls the total operations of the cell must have proper building materials with which to work. However, the presence of all the necessary compounds essential for life does not guarantee that life will spontaneously arise. All that will be assured is that existing life will continue if the other conditions necessary for life are present. Dr. Larry Butler, professor of biochemistry at Purdue University, tells how he likes to issue the following challenge to his students and biochemist colleagues:

> Assume any primordial soup you wish, with all the organic chemicals you specify—including enzymes, nucleic acids, sugars, or whatever you like, as long as they are not living. The mixture must be sterile, of course, to prevent bacterial contamination. Assume also any kind of atmosphere you wish, including any system. Then assume any kind of energy source you wish—electrical sparks, heat, ultraviolet light, or any known form of energy. Now show, either analytically or experimentally, that a truly living organism will arise out of this set of materials.[4]

Needless to say, no one has successfully accepted the challenge.

The only logical conclusion, it would seem, is that the earth has been carefully created to support life. There are too many conditions necessary for life that are found only on the earth to assume that all these conditions could be the results of undesigned, nonpurposive evolutionary chemical reactions.

There simply is no parallel in the nonliving world that begins to compare to the quality of the living world. Life is able to exist at a level unknown anywhere else in the universe. The living organisms of earth are unique in their existence.

> Inanimate nature stops at the low level organization of simple molecules. But living systems go on and combine molecules to form macromolecules, macromolecules to form organelles (such as nuclei, mitochondria, chloroplasts, ribosomes, and membranes) and eventually put these all together to form the greatest wonder of creation, a cell, with its astounding inner regulations. Then it goes on putting cells together to form "higher organisms" and increasingly more complex individuals ... at every step, new and more complex individuals and subtle qualities are created, and so in the end we are faced with properties which have no parallel in the inanimate world.[5]

Ancient Atmospheric Temperatures

The atmosphere plays a vitally important role in sustaining life on the earth. It contains not only the right composition necessary to support life, but also maintains constant conditions to assure the perpetuation of life. It does this through its many cycles—oxygen, nitrogen, carbon, water and others. Without these important cycles, many major elements would soon be locked up and not available for the use of organisms yet to be born.

Helmut E. Landsberg, an evolutionist, has determined that the earth's atmosphere has undergone at least four major changes (see "The Origin of the Atmosphere," *Scientific American*, August, 1953). The first stage, he believes, developed as the earth itself was formed from a molten mass with an exceedingly high temperature. This first atmosphere consisted primarily of ammonia-methane with traces of bromine, chlorine, fluorine, and sulfur. Atmospheric temperatures would have been over 14,000°F. At this temperature, "this rather unhealthy mixture could not have lasted for very long." It must have vanished almost instantly as geological time goes.

In a very short geologic period of time, the second atmosphere came into existence. It was formed primarily by volcanic activity and was composed mostly of water, carbon dioxide, and hydrogen. This is similar to the present volcanic gas composition which has been measured at 69 percent water vapor, 13 percent carbon dioxide, and 8 percent hydrogen. Landsberg believes that the surface temperatures were still well into the hundreds of degrees.

But under no circumstances could proteins have formed in these high temperatures. Proteins begin to break down at about 120°F. and are virtually destroyed at temperatures above 140°F. Also, at temperatures above 212°F., water could not exist in a liquid state. Protein formation (according to Stanley Miller) has to take place in an ammonia-methane atmosphere. But according to Landsberg's reasoning, such an atmosphere could not have existed at this proposed evolutionary stage. Even at the second stage, the atmosphere was so hot that water could not have existed on the surface of the earth. Without a water environment, protein synthesis, even if it were possible, could not have occurred as suggested by the theory of evolution.

Landsberg believes that as the atmospheric temperatures continued to cool down, liquid water eventually formed on the surface. When the surface temperatures reached about 160°F., the oceans of today were formed. This third atmosphere consisted of approximately 74 percent carbon dioxide, 15 percent water vapor, and 10 percent nitrogen. It was at this time, Landsberg suggests, that life arose abiogenetically.

Landsberg also believes it was during the third stage cells began producing oxygen which changed the atmosphere into its final stage—the atmosphere of today. He follows the evolutionary line of thinking by stating that cells simply developed necessary cholorplasts and were thus able to produce oxygen. No attempt has been made to explain just how these cells managed to develop chloroplasts.

Dr. George Simpson believes that present atmospheric conditions on the earth are not different from those of three billion years ago. He further believes that the oceans were in existence as far back as that time and that they were influenced by the same erosional processes observed today:

> It is established that approximately 3 billion years ago the earth had a solid, cool crust and that processes of rock oxidation, weathering, and erosion were already going on. This means that there was already water on the surface and that the atmosphere cannot have been extremely different from what it is now.[6]

Ernst J. Öpik, astronomer at the Armagh Observatory in Northern Ireland, also believes that the present composition of the earth's atmosphere has been basically the same for the past three billion years. He states that traces of primitive plants in very ancient rocks of Canada and South Rhodesia "suggest that the climate of the earth three billion years ago was not radically different from what it is now."[7]

But Öpik is convinced that there have been major climatic changes due to variations in the energy output of the sun. He does not believe, however, that any of the present proposals— dust clouds from volcanic explosions, changes in the tilt or orbit of the earth, and so on—adequately explain the climatic changes other than solar energy variations. He bases his theory on the varying amount of metals in the sun's core. As these metals collect around the core of the sun, they reduce the energy output of the sun by considerable amounts. He believes that as the metals are gradually destroyed by the heat and pressure of the sun's interior, there is a gradual warming effect over the entire earth. His theory, he admits, only holds true if the metals in the core of the sun total at least three percent of the sun's mass. But evidence so far has failed to support his hypothesis. Most authorities put the amount of metals in the sun at less than one tenth of one percent—3,000 times less than what Öpik's theory requires.

According to Öpik's theory, the early earth did not begin with a temperature in the thousands of degrees F., but rather well below freezing. He feels that a gradual warming has occurred since the origin of the earth.

I believe that the work of Landsberg, Miller, Öpik, as well as many other evolutionists, merely serves to demonstrate that evolutionary theories concerning the origin of the earth only contradict each other, lack any real evidence, and have failed to explain anything.

The Gaea Hypothesis

The remarkable ability of the earth to sustain life has caused some scientists to wonder just how it is able to do so. Admittedly, there are no inorganic chemical reactions that even begin to compare with the remarkable chemistry of protoplasm—there is simply nothing else like it. For life to have survived on the planet Earth for the proposed billion or so years would require an unbelievably long equilibrium state in the *biosphere* (areas of the earth's atmosphere, hydrosphere,

Variation Within Evolutionary Theories on Ancient Earth Temperatures
Landsberg vs. Öpik

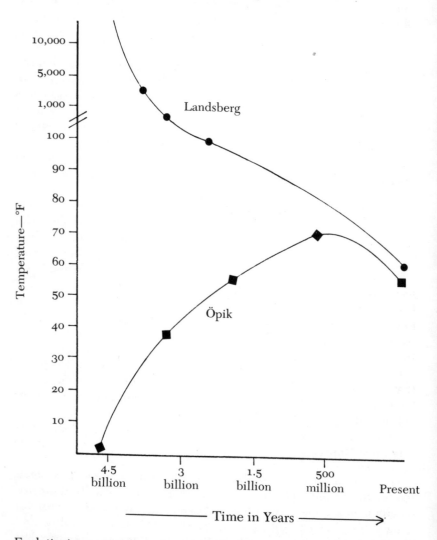

Evolutionists cannot agree upon proposed ancient climates and temperatures on the early earth. Great contradictory variation exists in the many evolutionary theories.

and lithosphere in which life may be found). The oxygen, nitrogen, and carbon dioxide levels of the atmosphere as well as the mineral composition of the oceans would have to remain constant during this long period of time. Any change in any one of the elements or compounds would have a drastic effect on the living conditions of the earth.

It would seem that in a billion years, assuming that evolution is correct, there would have been major compositional changes in the atmosphere and oceans. Yet geologic records indicate that no such changes have occurred. This remarkable steady-state condition has caused some scientists to propose the *Gaea hypothesis.*

The *Gaea hypothesis* refers to the earth's biosphere as a single entity that functions like an organism itself. The hypothesis is named after the ancient Greek goddess of Earth, Gaea. She was to have given birth to the first members of the human race as well as to the first of the Greek gods.

The Gaea hypothesis proposes that the biosphere has the unique ability to compensate for changes that occur which would have detrimental effects upon life. This hypothesis almost gives the biosphere characteristics of life itself. In a billion years, the intensity of solar radiation coming from the sun would have had measurable effects upon the earth's atmosphere. Any increase of radiation would break down the ozone layer, allowing fatal doses of ultraviolet radiation to reach Earth's surface. The Gaea hypothesis suggests that the earth's biosphere is able to compensate, somehow, for any sudden increases in solar radiation so that life continues to exist.

Gaea theorists suggest their hypothesis is supported by the fact that the geologic record shows temperature changes on the earth have been relatively small compared to variations in the solar energy output during the earth's history.

Various evolutionists have suggested that the sun has changed its brightness and heat output since its origin. Estimates are that there have been anywhere from a doubling to a tripling of solar energy output during the proposed evolutionary history of the solar system. Yet paleontological studies of life on the earth do not demonstrate drastic temperature changes. Estimates of temperatures during the Ice Age dropped by only 10°C. to 20°C.

Dr. Verschuur of the Fiske Planetarium in Boulder, Colorado, has pointed out that the oceans have remained at a fairly constant degree of acidity for about 3.5 billion years. This is remarkable, since it is known that marine organisms have a definite effect on the oceans' acidic levels.

> Another constancy found in nature is that the oceans of the earth apparently have been at about the same degree of acidity for about 3.5 billion years. Since acids of one sort or another are constantly being generated by plant life, it is remarkable that the generation of substances such as ammonia, which can neutralize these acids, has also been kept at such a level that the oceans have never become too acidic for life to survive.[8]

Dr. Verschuur supports the belief that an oxygen-free (reducing atmosphere) condition as proposed by Oparin was necessary in order for the development of life from the nonliving (spontaneous generation) to have taken place. He says there is fossil evidence that supports his hypothesis:

> The first living things that existed between 3 to 4 billion years ago needed no oxygen for their survival. This we know from the study of fossils of those times.[9]

However, an oxygen-free atmosphere would not have allowed current life forms to exist. Furthermore, the fossil record shows the sudden appearance of nearly every major phyla of today. It does not indicate an oxygen-free atmosphere but an atmosphere very similar in composition to that of today. Evolutionists have proposed that Earth's early atmosphere was rich in ammonia as well as methane and water. Dr. Verschuur admits that such an atmosphere would only result in producing a "significant greenhouse effect."

The carbon dioxide atmosphere found on Venus has caused a greenhouse effect that has raised the surface temperature of that planet to over 700°F. If ammonia is also capable of producing a significant greenhouse effect, then evolutionists are now facing an additional dilemma. Protein will denature (break down) in high temperatures (120°F. and above). If the ammonia atmosphere proposed by evolutionists for the early earth created a greenhouse effect, which it would according to Dr. Verschuur, then amino acids would be unable to form lasting proteins—the heat on the surface would have broken them down as soon as they were formed, assuming they could form in the first place.

The Gaea hypothesis may be an interesting attempt to explain how life could have existed for so long on Earth since organisms need steady-state conditions for their survival. But this hypothesis has

only presented more insurmountable problems for the evolutionists
and their various theories.

Comparison Between an Oxidizing and Reducing Atmosphere

ELEMENT	OXIDIZING ATMOSPHERE (contains free oxygen)	REDUCING ATMOSPHERE (no free oxygen)
Carbon	Carbon dioxide (CO_2)	Methane (CH_4) Carbon dioxide (CO_2)
Hydrogen	Water (H_2O)	Hydrogen (H_2)
Nitrogen	Nitrogen (N_2)	Ammonia (NH_3) Nitrogen (N_2)
Oxygen	Oxygen (O_2) Water (H_2O)	Water (H_2O)

Many evolutionists have assumed that since an oxidizing atmosphere, like
our present atmosphere, would have prevented spontaneous generation,
then the early atmosphere of the earth must have been a reducing atmosphere—one free of oxygen. There is no way to prove that such an atmosphere ever existed, though there is evidence to suggest that such an
atmosphere could never have existed.

5. BIOGENESIS— LIFE FROM LIFE

Life can only come from life. This is the basic principle for biogenesis. The word *biogenesis* (Greek, "life-origin") was coined by T. H. Huxley in 1870 to express "the hypothesis that living matter always arises by the agency of preexisting living matter." Opposite of biogenesis is *abiogenesis*—"life from the nonliving."

There are no known exceptions to the principle of biogenesis. It is the foundation upon which much understanding of biological processes rests. However, in spite of this knowledge, many evolutionists still maintain that at one time in the past, life must have arisen spontaneously from nonliving substances—abiogenetically. George Wald believes that the spontaneous origin of life from the nonliving was a virtual certainty. He has stated that the spontaneous generation of life "belongs in the category of at-least-once phenomena."[1]

There was a time when practically all leading authorities of science adhered to the concept of spontaneous generation. This theory held that it was possible for life simply to arise from nonliving substances. Aristotle (384–322 B.C.) taught that fleas and mosquitoes came from putrefying matter. An eminent seventeenth century scientist was certain he had seen rats develop from old rags. Van Helmont in the sixteenth century believed that scorpions would arise spontaneously from crushed basil:

> Scoop out a hole in a brick. Put into it some sweet basil, crushed. Lay a second brick upon the first so that the hole may be perfectly covered. Expose the two bricks to the sun, and at the end of a few days the smell of the sweet basil, acting as a ferment, will change the herb into real scorpions.

Between 1859 and 1861, Louis Pasteur proved as conclusively as science can that in the modern world, no living thing arises except from other living things. Pasteur satisfactorily demonstrated to the scientific community that microorganisms are carried through the air and that spontaneous generation does not occur in any case. His work marked the beginning of the principle of biogenesis.

Before Pasteur's time, very few scientists would deny that life came from the nonliving: worms from mud, maggots from decaying meat, mice from various kinds of refuse, and so on. Aristotle believed in spontaneous generation as did Newton, William Harvey, Descartes, van Helmont, and many others. Even some theologians believed in spontaneous generation. The English Jesuit John Turberville Needham carefully explained that God did not actually create the plants and most animals directly, but "He bade the earth and waters to bring them forth." Needham concluded that there was nothing heretical in ascribing to the theory of spontaneous generation.

But, step by step, in a controversial battle that lasted almost two centuries, spontaneous generation was finally reduced to a myth and placed outside the realm of science. Francesco Redi showed that maggots do not develop from putrefying meat, but from flies that lay their eggs on the meat. He demonstrated this by placing a screen over the meat so that no flies could get to it. As long as the screen remained, no maggots developed on the meat.

A century later Lazzaro Spallanzani, an Italian abbe, showed that a nutritive broth would not develop microorganisms if it were sealed off from the air while boiling. The objection to his experiment was that in boiling the broth, Spallanzani had actually rendered the broth completely incompatible with conditions necessary for life. When Spallanzani broke open the seals, allowing air to rush in, the broth began to rot. Many believed that the new air revived the conditions necessary for spontaneous generation. Spallanzani was never able to overcome this problem in his experiment.

In 1860 Louis Pasteur made a simple modification of Spallanzani's experiment. He boiled broth in flasks but instead of sealing them off, he drew out the neck of the flask into a long S-shaped curve and left the end open to the air. Air was able to pass back and forth freely, but heavier particles of dust, bacteria and molds would collect on the walls of the curved neck, only rarely reaching the broth. In such a flask the broth seldom was contaminated.

Wald feels that the downfall of spontaneous generation has left science at a loss to account for the origin of life (see "The Origin of Life," *Scientific American*, August, 1954). The implications of the

Pasteur's Experiment

Pasteur's modification of Spallanzani's experiment proved that fermentation or putrefaction is the result of air-borne organisms, not spontaneous generation. The specially designed S-shaped flasks contained a nutritive broth that was subject to prolonged heating to kill all organisms. The mouth of the flask was left open. Pasteur found that no organisms reached the broth, since any that entered the opening would fall to the floor of the neck and rem[a] there. Days, weeks, months, and even years could pass without any putre[f]tion occurring.

work of Redi, Spallanzani and Pasteur have utterly destroyed theory of spontaneous generation.

For those who choose to reject both spontaneous generation supernatural creation, there are no other alternatives. One eith cepts the origin of life as the result of supernatural creation or result of spontaneous generation.

The study of the origin of life may be profitable from a phil[o]cal point of view, but such a study simply lies outside the r[e] science. Yet any theory that deals with the origin of life—a

lution certainly does—must provide a reasonable explanation as to how life began. For the creationist, the first life form was the result of a creative act of an Eternally Divine Being. Granted, there are no scientific ways to prove this, but still, such a belief is consistent with the law of biogenesis. What better explanation for the origin of life than the result of the careful planning of the Eternal Life Source, God!

Protein Synthesis

Proteins are made of smaller units called *amino acids*. There are 20 different amino acids commonly found in proteins, although their total number may be considerably larger than this. Proteins are very complex organic substances and cannot be made by simply mixing amino acids in a test tube and presto—proteins!

Protein synthesis is carefully governed by a special class of other proteins called *enzymes*. These organic catalysts greatly accelerate chemical reactions in the body and play such a dominant role in the chemistry of life that it is extremely difficult to imagine the existence of life without them. Practically every chemical reaction occurring within the cell is the result of these catalytic enzymes. Without them, life simply would not exist.

Enzymes, in turn, are formed at the direction of the DNA within the nuclei of the cells. Messenger ribonucleic acids (RNA) receive the message or code for the specific enzyme needed from the DNA and carry it to the ribosomes in the cytoplasm of the cell. At these sites specific enzymes are manufactured for specific tasks. Once the enzyme performs its function, it reverts back to the original amino acids that made it up. The components then await further directions from the RNA messengers. Specific proteins are always manufactured by the cell for each specific task. Not just any protein will do—it can only be the right protein for the right job.

DNA also represents the genetic material for all organisms. These extremely complex molecules are so sensitive to the world outside the protection of the cell that it is inconceivable that they could ever exist apart from the cell. Only through the DNA is the cell able to develop, maintain itself, preserve its identity, and reproduce its kinds.

Proteins need enzymes in order to exist. Enzymes are produced only at the direction of the DNA. Without the messenger RNA, the

proper protein will not be formed and the needed cellular task will remain undone. Without the protection of the cell, neither DNA or RNA could exist. All are totally dependent upon each other. Without the enclosure of the cell, the huge molecules would not be able to exist. Yet without them, the cell itself could not exist. Dr. Harold Blum, a famous biochemist, admits that it is somewhat a mystery as to how all these essential substances came to exist. He believes that only by a miracle could such complexity have happened:

> The more we study living systems, the more we marvel at their beautifully ordered complexity; and we may estimate that the forming of such systems (or even much simpler ones) by a single chance act would have an improbability of the order of a miracle that could have happened only once in our universe.[2]

It is possible that the wonders of the cell may never be completely understood. Biochemists and microbiologists admit that they do not fully understand it. And yet those who hold to the spontaneous generation theory insist that all the complex molecules that make up the cell, and that are so intricately dependent upon each other for their very existence, somehow managed to develop at random, without any direction, in a hostile world that would certainly bring about their destruction. Then, against all observed biological processes, these "organic" molecules somehow managed to become the first living cells.

Wald states that organic compounds are produced only by living organisms. With almost negligible exceptions, all the organic compounds in existence today were formed by living organisms. In 1828, Friedrich Wohler synthesized the first organic compound, urea. It was believed by many that Wohler demonstrated that organic compounds do not require living organisms to make them. But this simply is not the case. Professor Wald reminds his students that "organic chemists are alive; Wohler merely showed that they (chemists) can make organic compounds externally as well as internally."[3]

Thousands of hours of work have gone into trying to recreate conditions in the lab that evolutionists believe existed on the early earth. But no matter what conditions may be created in the lab, there is no way of proving that these are the very same conditions that existed at an earlier time on the earth.

In 1953 an article appeared in *Science* magazine entitled "A Production of Amino Acids Under Possible Primitive Earth Conditions"

(Vol. 117, May 15, 1953) by Stanley L. Miller. At the time, Stanley Miller was a graduate student of the Nobel laureate in chemistry, Harold Urey. Miller performed a simple experiment involving a mixture of water vapor (H_2O), methane (CH_4), ammonia (NH_3), and hydrogen (H_2)—all gases believed necessary for the formation of organic compounds. These gases were circulated over an electric spark continuously for a week. Water at one end of the apparatus was heated to the boiling point, circulating the vapor to the other end of the apparatus where it passed through the electric spark, then into a cooling jacket where it condensed. The water was then returned to the starting point, boiled again and the whole process repeated.

At one place on the apparatus condensed water was collected in a protective trap. At the end of the week the water in the trap was analyzed by special paper chromatography and found to contain a mixture of amino acids—glycine and alanine, the simplest and most prevalent amino acids in proteins.

Evolutionists felt that Miller's experiment provided evidence that life did originate in a spontaneous fashion. But Miller's experiment did *not* demonstrate the origin of life; it only demonstrated that man is capable of synthesizing amino acids by utilizing carefully controlled laboratory procedures.

Neither did Miller's experiment prove that the early atmosphere of the earth was made up of a methane-ammonia mixture. Dr. P. H. Abelson, geochemist and director of the Geophysical Laboratory at the Carnegie Institute of Washington, does not believe that existing geological conditions provide evidence that there ever was a primitive methane-ammonia atmosphere. He points out that there is much evidence to the contrary. He says that "an amount of ammonia equivalent to present atmospheric nitrogen would be destroyed, due to degradation by ultraviolet radiation, in about 30,000 years."[4]

Thirty thousand years is a mere drop in the bucket compared to the millions of years necessary for the origin of life as proposed by the theory of evolution. This would force evolution to operate at such a rapid rate that we should expect to see it happening before our very eyes today.

Dr. Gish, biochemist for the Institute for Creation Research in San Diego, further points out that solar radiation would have reduced methane to hydrophobic organic compounds which should be in evidence in the earth's earliest rocks, but no such compounds have been found.

Origin of Life Experiment by Stanley H. Miller

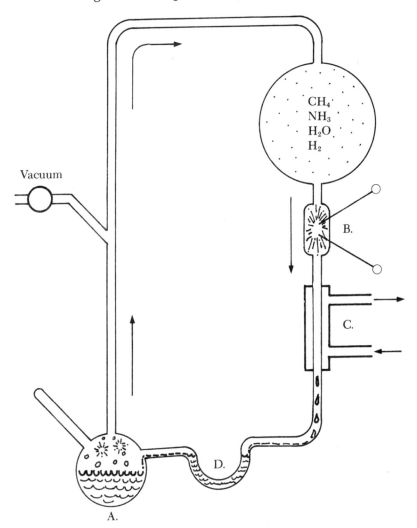

Water was brought to the boiling point at position A. The vapor circulated, carrying with it the other gases to position B where the various gases were exposed to an electrical charge. At position C a cooling jacket lowered the temperature so that condensation occurred. Position D represents the cold trap. At the end of one week, water in the cold trap showed the presence of two different amino acids.

Summary of the Abiogenic Theory of the Origin of Life

Step 1. Early atmosphere of H_2O, CH_4, NH_3

Step 2.

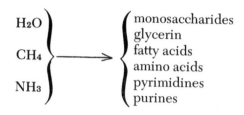

$$H_2O$$
$$CH_4 \longrightarrow$$
$$NH_3$$

monosaccharides
glycerin
fatty acids
amino acids
pyrimidines
purines

Step 3. Self-replicating molecules form macromolecules

monosaccharides → polysaccharides
fatty acids + glycerin → fats + lipids
amino acids → proteins → enzymes
pyrimidines and purines
+ ribose + phosphate → nucleotides
nucleotides → nucleic acids → nucleoproteins

Step 4. Formation of early cells
nucleoproteins + organic shells → early cells

Step 5. Development of photosynthesis
early cells + chlorophyll → photosynthesis
photosynthesis → oxygen in present atmosphere

The abiogenic theory of the origin of life is based upon the assumption that it could happen. It cannot be demonstrated in the lab, nor can it be observed in nature. Simple molecules do not evolve into complex molecules. There are no known self-replicating molecules in nature. There is no evidence to support the abiogenic origin of life.

Precambrian iron ores of the Vermillion range in Minnesota are greatly oxidized, a process which took place early in the earth's history and which shows that Earth's oldest rocks were subjected to an atmosphere containing oxygen, not methane and ammonia.

One, Two, Three—Punt!

The suggestion that the earth's early atmosphere was free of oxygen is, I believe, the result of more extralogical reasoning. It has been demonstrated that spontaneous generation cannot occur. However, it is possible to synthesize simple amino acids in carefully controlled experiments that utilize oxygen-free atmospheres. Therefore, many have concluded that the early atmosphere of the earth must also have been free of oxygen.

> ... it can be said that in spite of the elaborate hypotheses that have been proposed to justify the assumption that the earth had a reducing atmosphere, early in its history, this assumption is extremely tenuous and actually contraindicated by a considerable amount of evidence. The assumption that the earth at one time had a reducing atmosphere satisfies most people. This is so because most people subscribe to the following set of assumptions: since life exists, life evolved; evolution of life required a reducing atmosphere, therefore, the primitive earth must have had a reducing atmosphere.[5]

Dr. Gish has indicated that there are two serious flaws in Miller's experiment. The cold trap on the apparatus was designed to isolate the products of the reaction immediately after their formation. Without the trap, significant destruction of the amino acids would have occurred. The second flaw is that the amino acids were formed by the energy of electrical discharges in the atmosphere. If this were the actual case in the origin of life, the amino acids would have been destroyed by the sun's ultraviolet radiation before they reached the safety of the cold trap. The cold trap performed a major part in the success of Miller's experiment, but it should be noted that there is no counterpart in nature that parallels such a cold trap.

Just how did the evolutionists come to believe that the primitive atmosphere was composed of water vapor, methane, ammonia, and hydrogen? It is assumed that since amino acids resulted in an experiment that involved these gases, then nature, given the same atmosphere, is capable of doing the same thing.

Conditions have been created so as to harmonize with the theory. This is why evolution is nonfalsifiable; there is no way to test a theory that allows for the development of any condition that its proponents feel necessary to guarantee the success of the theory. If it is known that spontaneous generation has been proved impossible under observable conditions, then all one has to do is to change the conditions so that, at least in theory, it now becomes possible.

When scientists begin to adjust conditions in order to guarantee the success of a favorite theory, the "game" is no longer about science. We leave the realm of science entirely and work with imagination. No matter what objection may be raised, the evolutionist simply creates a hypothetical situation in which his theory just might work—even if there is no way to prove it.

Spontaneous Dissolution

Complex chemicals, particularly organic compounds such as proteins, do not increase in complexity if left alone but tend to break down. *Spontaneous dissolution*, the very opposite of spontaneous generation, demonstrates that any chemical process catalyzed by an enzyme will tend to go from complex to simple. In other words, complex organic compounds will always break down into component parts spontaneously. This is exactly what is expected according to the second law of thermodynamics.

Oxygen tends to denature proteins in addition to normal spontaneous dissolution. This is another reason why the evolutionist must assume that the early atmosphere had no free oxygen. It is impossible for complex organic compounds to exist in an environment that includes free oxygen. But how does one get rid of the oxygen in the atmosphere? Simply create a hypothetical condition that does not include oxygen! As long as you are no longer working with that which is observable, then you are free to create any situation your imagination allows. While you may not be able to prove that your oxygen-free atmosphere ever existed, no one will be able to prove that it did not.

The assumption that the early atmosphere was free of oxygen only creates an additional problem for the evolutionist. Without oxygen there would be no ozone. Without the protection of the ozone layer, it is doubtful that life could exist on the surface of the earth.

The evolutionist believes that anaerobic organisms (capable of existing in oxygen-free environments) somehow managed to develop chloroplasts. The hypothetical development of this extremely complex organelle would allow for the process of photosynthesis. The composition of the atmosphere would begin to change and no longer be free of oxygen. From the photosynthetically produced oxygen the protective ozone layer would develop. The major problem facing the evolutionist at this point is that no satisfactory theory has been proposed as to how (or why) these anaerobic organisms managed to develop chloroplasts.

It would certainly be no small matter for the anaerobic organisms to completely change their metabolism to accomodate the newly acquired atmospheric oxygen and somehow become aerobic organisms. From methane to ammonia to amino acids to proteins to anaerobic organisms to aerobic organisms—these are certainly no small steps! Evolutionists are unable to provide adequate explanations as to how these miraculous steps were made possible. There are no biological processes today that even begin to suggest that such improvements are possible. These steps are all uphill and always move from the simple to the complex.

Supplying the Energy Needs

In order for cells to carry on the activities of life, they must receive a constant supply of energy and building materials. Some mechanism must be present that is capable of harnessing the energy of the sun so that it can be directed into useful and available energy. Without this mechanism the cell will die and rapidly disintegrate. In our world today this mechanism is the chloroplasts in photosynthetic plants.

It has been suggested that pre-photosynthetic life forms, according to the theory of evolution, obtained their energy by *fermentation*— the process by which organisms derive energy by breaking down organic molecules. But in order to function, fermentation requires organic compounds such as sugars. These organic compounds are, with insignificant exceptions, formed only by living organisms. Again we see evidence of insurmountable problems within the theory of evolution. The organism needs organic compounds, but the organic compounds cannot be formed except by another organism. Both are dependent upon each other and both must be present at the same time.

Fermentation is not a process that leads to the evolution of simple chemicals into organisms, but rather is a process that is totally dependent on the living cell. Furthermore, fermentation is a very inefficient method of producing energy. Fermenting 180 grams of sugar will only release about 20,000 calories of energy. Respiration will release over 700,000 calories from the same 180 grams. An example of fermentation would be that of yeast acting on sugar. The process would appear as follows:

Fermentation

$$C_6H_{12}O_6 \rightarrow 2CO_2 + 2C_2H_5OH + energy$$
$$\text{(sugar)} \quad \text{(carbon dioxide)} \quad \text{(alcohol)}$$

The process of fermentation also tends to produce various poisonous waste products such as lactic acid, acetic acid, formic acid, and so on. Just what effect would these waste products have on the first anaerobic cells? According to Dr. Wald: " . . . if the organisms were ever to penetrate to the air and land, these products must prove a serious embarrassment."

Darwin Didn't Know Better

Darwin was unaware of the laws of thermodynamics and the laws of heredity, which were being formulated during his lifetime. But in light of what these laws teach us, we can no longer teach that spontaneous generation is a reality. Dr. A. E. Wilder Smith, professor of pharmocology at the University of Illinois Medical Center, Chicago, stated: "Darwin in his day could therefore assume with impunity that life did arise spontaneously. Today, in the light of scientific discovery, we can no longer do this."[6]

Dr. Simpson admits that spontaneous generation is certainly impossible today, but believes that if the conditions in the past were different from what they are today, the "earliest life forms could and almost certainly did arise from nonliving matter by a natural process." He therefore concludes that it is possible that spontaneous generation could have occurred: "there is, at least, nothing improbable in this view."[7]

Just what is it that we know today? For one thing, we know that the spontaneous generation theory has been utterly destroyed and reduced to its rightful place as nothing more than a myth. It has been proved in theory and experiment that abiogenesis is impossible.

Nevertheless, many evolutionists are convinced that we are the product of a spontaneous generation process.

But why would a scientist, with the knowledge that spontaneous generation is impossible, be willing to admit that we are here as a result of this very process? It is really quite simple—those who reject the Biblical account of creation are left with nothing except spontaneous generation.

There have been many attempts to reconstruct environments that may provide raw materials from which life might arise. Stanley Miller was able to produce certain amino acids in his demonstration, but he was a long way from producing a living organism. Dr. Henry Morris points out that amino acids are not living things in any sense and that the special precautions in Miller's experiment could not have existed on an early Earth.[8]

Viruses—Living or Not?

Viruses, regarded by some as a type of primordial life and believed to play an important role in the evolution of cells, appear to be on the borderline between living cells and nonliving chemicals. But it is seriously doubted that viruses can qualify as living organisms or borderline living organisms. They are totally dependent upon living cells in order to multiply themselves. The actual multiplication of the viral units is done by the invaded cell. The nucleic acids of the cell manufacture the new viruses. This is done when the cellular nucleic acids receive the incorrect code from the viral nucleic acid and incorrectly duplicate the viral nucleic acid rather than the cellular nucleic acid. Viruses cannot even reproduce themselves—it must be done for them by a living cell. Dr. Gish has done extensive research into the question of whether viruses are living entities and has drawn the following conclusion:

> Viruses are nothing more than complex organic chemical molecules, consisting of an inner core of nucleic acid (either DNA or RNA) and an outer protein coat (some viruses are accompanied by a small amount of carbohydrates and lipids, which are nothing more than cell debris). A virus possesses not a single enzyme, not a trace of metabolic activity, no energy, no source of building blocks. Not by any stretch of the imagination could a virus be considered a living thing, primitive or other-

wise. A virus is simply a nucleoprotein (a complex of nucleic acid with a protein). When a virus gets into a susceptible cell, it, like many other nucleoproteins contained within a cell, is replicated by this cell, the complex synthetic and energy-producing mechanism contained within the cell being utilized for this purpose.[9]

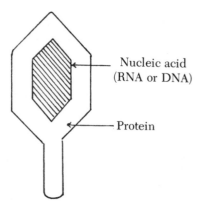

A typical Virus. This is only one shape. Many others are known to exist.

No Self-replicating Molecules

Dr. Gish states that no self-replicating molecules exist on the earth. Neither nucleic acids nor proteins possess such an ability. He states: "there is no molecule of any kind that possesses such a property, neither can one imagine a structure that would invest a molecule with such an ability."[10]

Yet millions of science students are taught each year that nucleoproteins can self-replicate and that it was through this very process that the first cell came to exist. Perhaps students should ask for examples of observed self-replicating molecules.

Much attention was given to the work of J. P. Danielli in 1970 when he was reported to have synthesized a living cell. But it should be noted that Dr. Danielli started with living cells, disassembled them, and then refabricated a cell from the parts of the dismantled cells. Although it is a notable accomplishment, it cannot claim to have created life.

Today, after many experiments, there is not even the slightest scientific evidence that abiogenesis is possible—life simply does not come from nonlife! But just for a moment, let's consider what would actually be proved if a scientist were to synthesize life. Would it prove that nature could do the same thing?

> But even if, someday, (the synthesis of life) is accomplished, that achievement will not prove that the same thing happened by chance three billion years ago. Rather, it will prove, if anything, that an exceedingly high concentration of intelligent planning and precisely controlled laboratory apparatus were necessary for the accomplishment.[11]

Abiogenetic Theory of Self-replicating Molecules

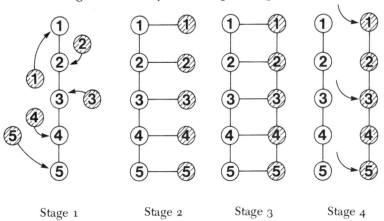

Stage 1   Stage 2   Stage 3   Stage 4

Stage 1. Preexisting nucleoprotein (light shading) are surrounded by raw material necessary for the construction of another nucleoprotein.

Stage 2. Raw material matches up with the preexisting nucleoprotein.

Stage 3. Correctly positioned raw material lined up with corresponding parts of preexisting nucleoprotein.

Stage 4. Newly formed nucleoprotein (dark shading) separates from the original "model." The model and replica are identical in composition.

Diagrams such as the above are commonly found in texts that deal with the evolutionary origin of life. There are, however, no such self-replicating molecules known to exist anywhere in the world.

The synthesis of life, should this ever become possible, would only be further proof that life can only come from life—that of the scientist conducting the experiment. Would this really be an example of biogenesis? Try removing the living element—the scientist—from the experiment and see how far the experiment will proceed on its own!

6. GENETIC MUTATIONS

A major problem facing the theory of evolution is that it contradicts the laws of thermodynamics, in particular the second law—the law of entropy. There are no physical or biological systems that lie outside the laws of thermodynamics. According to R. B. Lindsay (*American Scientist*, 1968), "there is a general natural tendency of all observed systems to go from order to disorder, reflecting dissipation of energy available for future transformation—the law of increasing entropy."

All physical and biological processes show an increase of entropy that measures the randomness, or lack of orderliness, of the system. The greater the randomness, the greater the entropy.

Nevertheless, Sir Julian Huxley maintains that evolution has somehow managed to provide greater complexity as time passes. Huxley stated that evolution is not a random process, but a "directional" and "irreversible" process that always increases the complexity of the organism.

> Evolution in the extended sense can be defined as a directional and essentially irreversible process occurring in time, which in its course gives rise to an increase of variety and an increasingly high level of organization in its products. Our present knowledge indeed forces us to view that the whole of reality is evolution—a single process of self-transformation.[1]

The theory of evolution is at a complete loss to explain how complexity results from randomness—how simple organisms have managed to become more complex. It was believed at one time that Darwin's natural selection could account for such increase in complexity, but it is now known that natural selection is not capable of producing an increase in complexity. If anything, natural selection preserves the species—it may help eliminate the weak and the "unfit," but it cannot improve the genetic potential of the species.

Biston Betularia—The Peppered Moth

The example of the peppered or Kettlewell's moth in England has been heralded by many evolutionists as the most striking evolutionary change ever witnessed by man. Before the industrial revolution in England, the peppered moth, *Biston betularia*, population consisted primarily of the light-colored variety, whereas the dark-colored variety made up only a small percentage of the population. Gradually, as factories began to belch their pollutants from huge smoke stacks, the trees and rocks turned darker in color, making it easy for birds to spot the light-colored peppered moths against the darker background, but giving more protection to the dark-colored variety. As would be expected, the population began to shift so that today about 95 percent of the peppered moths are of the dark-colored variety in the industrial areas of England.

While this is a fine example of natural selection at work, it does not even begin to prove the evolutionary process. Dr. L. Harrison Matthews wrote in the introduction to Darwin's *Origin of Species* that the *Biston betularia* experiment in no way gives support to the theory of evolution. He cautions the reader against accepting this experiment as proof of evolution " . . . for however the population may alter in their content of light, intermediate, or dark forms, all the moths remain from beginning to end *Biston betularia*."[2]

It now appears that *Biston betularia* is beginning to reverse its so-called "evolution." With the emphasis on a cleaner environment, England is beginning to reduce the amount of pollutants entering the air that have for so long discolored foliage and tree trunks and rocks. The result is the dark-colored peppered moths are becoming more visible and the light-colored ones appear to be increasing. However, there were only two major varieties of peppered moths to begin with, and today there are still only these same two varieties. There is no reason to believe that one variety is now in the process of becoming an entirely different species. *Biston betularia* is today the same *Biston betularia* that it was before the industrial revolution.

Natural selection preserves the species; but it does not have the ability to change one species into another species. It can only assure that the most fit will be able to survive.

The only mechanism capable of producing changes in a species or leading to the development of a new species or kind of organism is genetic mutation. But, as we shall see, not a single beneficial genetic mutation has ever been observed.

Genetic Mutations—All Go Downhill

Heredity is the process by which an organism reproduces itself in its progeny. It is controlled by the chromosomes within the nuclei of the sex cells, or gametes. On the chromosomes are the units of self-reproduction, the genes. The offspring will receive half of its genetic make-up from one parent and half from the other parent. There is no way, however, to know which half will come from which parent. The genetic combinations that are possible when conception occurs are beyond human comprehension. Infinite varieties are possible. The human body is controlled by no less than 23 pairs of chromosomes, and each chromosome may possess thousands of gene units.

Just for the sake of time, let's assume that there are only 1,000 genes in the entire human genetic structure. Even with this extremely conservative number, segregation and recombination would be capable of producing 2^{1000} different gene combinations in the individual. To give an idea of the immensity of this number, realize that there are approximately only 10^{130} electrons in the entire universe!

Naturally, one expects and finds a tremendous variety of characteristics within the human population. Except for the case of identical twins, variation is expected. No two persons are exactly alike. We are all different due to the rich combining potential of our genetic make-up. And as to be expected, in a common genetic pool individuals will tend to resemble each other and share certain characteristics that may be common to that population. Still, no two will ever be exactly alike.

Animal breeders learned long ago that animals tend to produce offspring that bear the same traits. Through patient work, breeders have carefully selected and bred animals until today we have a rich variety of horses, cattle, dogs, etc. Flower growers discovered that it is possible to crossbreed certain plant types to produce hybrids of the two parent types. Often, however, the hybrids are less fertile and viable than the parent stock. Some may even be totally sterile. Sterility seems to occur more often in animal hybrids than in plants.

Hybrids tend not to maintain on their own, but to produce progeny similar to the parent stock. Only by constant control over the breeding of animals are the desirable traits of the hybrids maintained. Hybrids should not be considered as examples of evolution since they do not involve genetic alterations in the form of mutations.

Neither is variety necessarily the result of mutated genes. Given a hypothetical situation involving only four genes, a variety is still possible without the results of mutation. Assigning letters to our hypothetical four genes, we might end up with P-gene, T-gene, S-gene, and O-gene. Assume now that there are only five viable combinations possible from the four genes: POST; TOPS; POTS; SPOT; and STOP. Without any mutations, these four genes are able to convey several different concepts, one of which may be capable of "holding water," POTS, while the others cannot.

Genes are considered to be very stable units because the copy they make in self-reproduction is a true likeness of the original in almost every case. But occasionally the copying process may be faulty and a new genetic structure emerges that is different from its model. This new structure may be known as a *mutation*. Mutations may be caused by exposure to X-rays, ultraviolet rays, high temperatures, or certain chemicals. Observed mutations have always proven to be harmful and even lethal to the organism. The genetic make-up of an organism is extremely complex, and even the slightest alterations within its structure proves everything but beneficial.

Occasionally a bacteria strain will show up that seems to be resistent to past methods of vaccination. We commonly read about a "new" form of gonorrhea that is resistant to penicillin or a "new" DDT-resistant insect pest that has farmers completely baffled. It is commonly reported, though incorrectly, that these resistant forms are examples of genetic mutations, because the parent stock was highly affected by penicillin or DDT as the case may be. But this is not proof that a beneficial genetic mutation has occurred. In fact, it is not proof of mutation at all.

The resistance is more likely the result of a genetic combination that has not been able to express itself in the past. Just as in the simple hypothetical examples of the four genes, POTS can hold water while the others cannot. When the environment changes so that it is now necessary for the hypothetical organism with the four genes to have to "hold water," POTS will now have an opportunity to express itself while the others may be adversely affected. Resistance probably is just another example of the infinite variety possible within the genetic potential of a given species.

Our alphabet of only 26 letters has given the English language about half a million words. One hardly thinks, however, that when a new word appears, it is the result of a mutation of a letter, but rather a new combination of letters that simply has not been used or accepted before but is now expressing itself.

It Just Isn't So!

An article on organic evolution, written by Harold L. Shapiro for Collier's Encyclopedia (1970), claims that new and different strains of corn and wheat or breeds of horses and cattle are evidence of experimental evolution.[3] But as already pointed out, a great variety will occur through genetic combinations. Selective breeding produces offspring having desirable characteristics, but this is not an example of evolution at work. Varieties within a horse-type, cattle-type, or flower-type are not indications of progressive evolution leading to the development of a new plant or animal. Horizontal variation does occur, but this is not evolution. Evolution requires a type of vertical variation that will end up producing a totally new species or type of plant or animal.

Shapiro further states that through the use of X-rays and chemicals, the process of evolution may be speeded up. This implies that it will now be possible to observe the actual change of one life-type into a completely new and improved life-type.

> . . . evolution on a laboratory scale has been productive not only in combining existing hereditary characters in new ways but also in producing new characters or mutations not present in the parents and available as material for new lines of evolutionary change. . . . It has also been found that the process can be artificially speeded up by such means as the use of X-rays or mustard gas.[4]

Radiation experiments have been performed on the common fruit fly, *Drosophila melanogaster*, for many years and have succeeded in producing countless numbers of fruit flies bearing mutations. Work using *Drosophila* began in 1911 when professor T. H. Morgan, then at Columbia University, began using them for genetic studies. This little fruit fly with the big scientific name requires only ten to 20 days to complete a generation, and one pair of parents may produce several hundred offspring. It would not be an exaggeration to say that more has been learned about the laws of heredity from the study of this one organism than from the work on all other organisms combined.

Great variation has been produced in *Drosophila* by irradiation, but in all the years of experimentation not a single beneficial improvement has been observed. There have been no changes to indicate that *Drosophila* is in the process of becoming anything other than what it is—a fruit fly. Although geneticists have been working with *Drosophila* for many years, it is still *Drosophila* today. It has not evolved into a new type of fruit fly.

Another hopeful for the evolutionist was the result of an experiment in which a cross was made between a radish and a cabbage, producing a plant called *Raphanobrassica*, which was distinct from the radish and the cabbage. It appeared to be capable of indefinite continuation without artificial segregation, as is often the case with hybrids.

At one time, evolutionists believed that *Raphanobrassica* could possibly serve as proof of evolution, but such was not the case. All this experiment did was to question the concept of species. No genetic mutations occurred with the cross of the radish and the cabbage. The "new" plant was the result of cross-fertilization and did not involve mutated genes. *Raphanobrassica* is nothing more than a hybrid, an example of horizontal variation, not vertical variation that would eventually produce a new plant or animal kind. The geneticist who produced the hybrid *Raphanobrassica* was not working with a new set of genes, but only with a new combination of existing genes. The simple re-arrangement of the furniture within a house may give it an entirely new perspective, but it has not led to the creation of a new dwelling type.

Genetic mutation is the ultimate source of all genetic variations found in natural populations and is the only explanation of how new material becomes available for natural selection to work on. Although Darwin wrote the *Origin* without the knowledge of genetic mutations, leading evolutionists of today lean very heavily upon mutations as the only mechanism capable of producing change.

Genetic mutations are a fact—they do exist. But unlike the evolutionists, the creationists believe that these disorders in the genetic code do not give rise to greater complexity that, in turn, leads to a new and more advanced animal or plant kind. The creationists believe, in accordance with the law of entropy, that all processes go with an increase in entropy or disorder. Complexity cannot be observed to rise out of disorder.

The Samaritans—Genetic Losers

Isolation does not lead to genetic improvement. Marriage between brother and sister is prohibited by law in this country because of the

The Samaritans

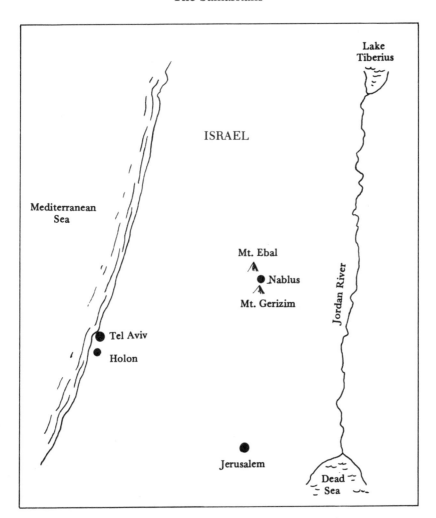

Modern Samaritan communities of Holon, south of Tel Aviv, and Nablus, located between the twin peaks of Mt. Ebal and Mt. Gerizim.

danger that both siblings would carry the same harmful recessive genes. There are, however, examples of what can happen when close family intermating occurs. But, as we will see, the results have not been a tendency toward beneficial changes. The Samaritans of today are examples of a small community of people who have managed to isolate themselves from the mainstream of the larger population in which they live. There are about 500 Samaritans living today. Approximately half live in the Nablus community in the valley bewteen the twin mountains of Ebal and Gerizim and the other half live in suburban Holon to the south of Tel Aviv.

According to a study by Shemaryahu Talmon (*Scientific American*, "The Samaritans", Vol. 236, January, 1977), the Samaritan communities are characterized by endogamous marriages. The results have been less than favorable. Some 27 percent of the Samaritans suffer from color blindness, and there is also a high level of respiratory deficiency, as indicated by chronic shortness of breath. In addition, the incidence of deaf-mutism is very high in these two communities.

Medical authorities and leading educators in the area are trying to educate young Samaritans to the dangers of community isolation and encouraging them to marry outside their community. If genetic isolation is supposed to produce new improved beneficial changes, then why isn't it working here?

Other "Benefits" of Genetic Mutations

Consider the observable evidence of genetic and chromosomal defects. Approximately 15 million Americans are affected by birth defects, and of these, some 12 million are the victims of diseases involving defects in the genes of chromosomes. There are more than 2,000 types of genetic conditions and birth defects, not a single one of which is held by physicians as beneficial! Consider further the following:

1. Of all spontaneous abortions (miscarriages), 36 percent are caused by gross chromosome defects (more than 100,000 per year).

2. At least 40 percent of all infant mortality is the result of genetic factors.

3. Genetic defects are present in nearly 5 percent of all live births.

4. About one third of all children admitted to hospital pediatric wards are there for genetic reasons.

5. Everyone carries between five and eight recessive genes for genetic disorders, and while the carrier may not be affected, disorders may occur in future generations.[5]

In addition to the above, many geneticists and physicians are beginning to find significant connections between genetic factors and a wide variety of diseases and disorders that were not previously considered to be genetically related. These include heart disease, certain forms of arthritis, cancer, and some forms of mental illness. Furthermore, the chances of higher incidences of genetic disease are *increasing*! Genetically speaking, the human race is not improving.

Approximately 2,000 genetic diseases and conditions are known to exist, and as many as 100 additional genetically related diseases and disorders are discovered every year. The following list of commonly found diseases and disorders refer only to conditions that are known to be genetically related:

GENETIC DISORDERS

CONDITION	INCIDENCE
Cleft lip/palate	1 in 1,000
Club foot	1 in 1,000
Cystic fibrosis	1 in 2,000
Diabetes	1 in 2,000
Down's syndrome	1 in 2,000
Hemophilia	1 in 10,000
Muscular dystrophy	1 in 20,000
Phenylketonuria (PKU)	1 in 10–20,000
Rh incompatibility	1 in 100
Sickle cell anemia	1 in 500
Tay-Sachs disease	1 in 3,600
Spina bifida	1 in 1,000

[6]

It seems incredible that the process which produces the above genetic disorders is the very process that caused a primordial cell to change over the eons of time into the complex organisms we observe today. It is interesting that after years of genetic research, not a single beneficial genetic mutation has ever been observed.

I believe it is safe to say that all known genetic mutations are harmful or injurious to the organism to some extent and seem to impair the fertility and viability of the organism. In addition, mutations are random and not directed.

Mutations are actually quite rare. Among the more than 2,000 genetic diseases and conditions known to exist in man, only a relatively few are commonly found in the general population. The frequency of rate of mutations in higher organisms would be somewhere between one in 10,000 and one in a million per gene per generation.

Evolutionists still insist that we are what we are today as the result of random genetic mutations. And we are told to believe this in spite of the lack of evidence and the fact that observable findings concerning genetic mutations have shown the impossibility of evolution. The modern neo-Darwinian theory of evolution cannot explain more than trivial variation, and utterly fails to explain just how a given animal or plant can evolve into a new species or genus. If random mutations are to be given serious consideration, then evolutionists must discover totally new natural laws, both physical and biological. Evolution simply cannot be justified in the light of present physical and biological laws.

Where's the Evidence?

Random alternations within the genetic structure of the cell will not lead to improvement. And yet if the evolutionist is asked to give an example of a beneficial mutation—one that is the result of a known genetic mutation that can be observed today—he is unable to do so. More likely than not he will list a harmful mutation and then offer the explanation that this may be harmful today, but it is possible that it may prove beneficial in the future. Without beneficial genetic mutations, there would be no possible way for evolution to occur. A leading evolutionist once gave as an example of a mutation the condition known as retinoblastoma—a cancer of the eye that affects children. The implication was that, though this might be harmful now, perhaps in the future it may be of benefit!

Since all observed mutations have proved harmful, why do evolutionists continue to insist that there are beneficial ones? They must do so because without beneficial genetic mutations, evolution could not have occurred. The observed genetic mutations have so far only produced hereditary diseases, various malformations and constitutional diseases.

Dr. James F. Crow, professor of genetics and chairman of the Department of Medical Genetics at the University of Wisconsin, has concluded that the overall effect of ionizing radiation has not improved the genetic structure of the human organism but has been detrimental in its effect: "Almost every mutation is harmful, and it is the individual who pays the price."[7]

If evolution occurs only through the mutant gene, shouldn't processes that produce genetic disorders be encouraged? Absolutely not! On this point the evolutionist must agree. While it may be acceptable to discuss the possible beneficial effects of genetic mutations, the evolutionist is very reluctant to expose himself, or any other member of the human race, to conditions that are known to cause genetic mutations. He knows that the results will not be beneficial.

Variation—Not Proof of Evolution

There is great variability in the human species, or for that matter, in any species. The beetles alone include some 250,000 species. Butterflies and moths total over 110,000 species. There are over 100,000 known species of fungi, 5,000 species of green algae, 3,000 species of sponges, 5,000 species of corals and their kin, 25,000 species of crustacea, 80,000 species of mollusks or shellfish, and over 300,000 species of plant life.

Evolutionists would have you to believe that variety is the result of genetic mutations. Mutations have proved, however, to be so harmful that variety is not likely due to mutant genes. The variability in the fossil record does not even match the proposed rate of evolutionary change.

Dr. Crow admits that while a great deal of variability does occur, it is not necessarily the result of evolution. He suggests that should evolution come to a total stop, variability would continue for thousands of generations.[8] Why then must we assume that we got this far by evolution when simple variation due to genetic combination potentials would be sufficient to account for all the observed variations? Variation is not proof of evolution. Fred J. Meldau, in his book *Why We Believe Creation, Not Evolution* (1959), reminds his readers that evolution clearly teaches the change, or transmutation, by way of the gradual process of mutation of one genus into another. Evolution is not concerned with the simple improvement of a given species, but rather the evolution of one species or genus into a new species or genus. Unless the evolutionist is able to substantiate his claim that a new genus can result from mutations within a simpler genus, always the higher from the lower, then his claims are invalid—that is, there is no evidence to support his claims.

What Is a Species?

There is no precise and acceptable definition of a species. It is usually defined as a group of animals or plants that are capable of interbreeding with each other and which rarely or never interbreed with other groups in nature. Lions (*Panthera leo*) and tigers (*Panthera tigris*) are known to interbreed in zoos, but in nature such interbreeding is not known to occur. Although they are known to be separate species, the common definition of a species may need to be reworked. The lion and the tiger do not appear to be as genetically specific as once believed. Perhaps it would be better to place lions and tigers in a *Panthera*-kind rather than in specific species.

Variations on small scales certainly can and do occur, but not on the scale that leads to innovations causing the development of a new species or kind. All variations are the result of existing genetic combinations that simply have not had an opportunity to express themselves in the phenotype in the past. This is how breeders of domestic animals have been able to develop, not create, new varieties. The genetic structure has always been present. Darwin observed great variation in the Galapago finches, but what he failed to note was that these variations were all within limits. He offered no evidence to suggest that a single Galapago finch was in the process of becoming anything but a finch.

There seems to be a limit as to how much variation can occur. Great variety exists within the dog-kind, but there is no evidence to suggest that a single variety of dog is becoming anything other than a dog. Perhaps Linnaeus may have carried his seven levels of classification one step too far. While species is commonly defined as "a category of similar, closely related organisms capable of interbreeding," this is of no consolation to biologists who are aware that the dog, wolf, coyote, fox, and jackal are all different species but are all capable of interbreeding. Likewise, the various cattle, buffalos, and bison interbreed, yet are assigned to different species.

This appears to be exactly what we find in the Genesis record of creation. There seems to be a boundary between dog-types and cattle-types that will never allow the two types to interbreed, but will allow for great variation within the many members of each type or kind. Some have claimed, including Darwin, that the Bible indicates fixity of species. But I do not believe this is the case. The Hebrew word for "kind" found in Genesis is *min* and refers to a related group capable of interbreeding and producing fertile offspring. *Min* seems to correspond more closely to the word "genera" than to species.

The Biblical definition of kind is certainly more consistent with what is being observed today, whereas the concept of species fails to hold up in too many cases. There are too many exceptions. Maybe it is time to change the concept of species to a more general kind at the genera level. Dog-kind seems to be able to interbreed as can cattle-kind, but there is a definite genetic boundary between dog-kind and cattle-kind. It seems that the Bible clearly teaches that in the original creation, several different kinds, having the potential to interbreed, may have been created rather than the specific species of our present classification system.

7. PROBLEMS IN THE FOSSIL RECORD

Fossils are found in almost all parts of the world. By *fossil* is meant the remains, the cast or form, of some organism, usually in petrified form. Fossils have been found on mountain tops, in the deepest valleys, on the plains, and even thousands of feet under the surface of the earth. In Oklahoma City, a fossil shell was brought up from a depth of 6,000 feet! In Bolivia, fossils have been found 12,000 feet above sea level.

Almost every living form today has been found in fossil form. Also, many extinct forms are found throughout the globe. Fossils are found in great abundance, sometimes piled like a log jam against each other. The fossil record does not speak, however, of a gradual evolutionary development of life but of mass death—sudden and worldwide.

The paleontologist bases much of his understanding of the past history of the earth on the fossils he finds. This record shows that life has been very abundant and greatly varied throughout the history of the earth. Many life forms are now found only as fossils and have no known living representatives. The dinosaurs are an extinct group of animals as are many of the fossils found in the earth's sedimentary rocks.

But the fossils themselves do not tell the paleontologist about their living conditions when the organisms were alive. This is left to the interpretation of the paleontologist. If all of his training has been based on the theory of evolution, then his conclusions will be a reflection of this evolutionary training. Many times a conclusion will be made that is not based on the observable evidence at hand, but rather on the philosophy of gradual development as proposed by the theory of evolution. The fossil record has not demonstrated a gradual development of complexity, as many textbooks on science suggest,

GEOLOGIC TIME TABLE

ERAS	PERIODS	YEARS AGO	DISTINCTIVE FEATURES
Cenozoic	Quaternary		
	Recent	25,000	Modern man
	Pleistocene	3,000,000	Early man; glaciation
	Tertiary		
	Pliocene	12,000,000	Large carnivores
	Miocene	25,000,000	First grazing mammals
	Oligocene	35,000,000	Large running mammals
	Eocene	60,000,000	Modern mammals
	Paleocene	70,000,000	First placental mammals
Mesozoic	Cretaceous	70,000,000	Climax of dinosaurs followed by extinction
	Jurassic	to	First birds
	Triassic	200,000,000	First dinosaurs
Paleozoic	Permian	200,000,000	Extinction of trilobites
	Pennsylvanian		First reptiles
	Mississippian		Sharks and amphibians
	Devonian	to	Fish and first amphibians
	Silurian		First terrestrial animal
	Ordovician		First fishes
	Cambrian	600,000,000	Trilobites
	Pre-Cambrian		Fossils consisting mainly of aquatic plants— rare

but rather a sudden appearance of life forms and a sudden destruction of life forms.

The fossil record is of little help to the evolutionist looking for the origin of life. There could be only two direct kinds of evidence: fossil remains of the first organisms or the rise of similar organisms today. Dr. Simpson admits that "no such fossils are known are are ever likely to be. . . ." The impossibility of spontaneous generation of life has already been discussed.

The fossil remains of billions of plants and animals suggest a rather sudden demise. What could have been responsible for creating such huge fossil graveyards? Charles Darwin could not help but wonder:

> It is impossible to reflect on the changed state of the American
> continent without the deepest astonishment. Formerly it must
> have swarmed with great monsters; now we find mere pigmies
> compared with the antecedent allied races. The greater num-
> ber, if not all of these extinct quadrupeds lived at a period and
> were the contemporaries of the existing sea shells. Since they
> lived, no very great changes in the form of the land can have
> taken place. What, then, has exterminated so many species and
> whole genera? The mind at first is irresistibly hurried into the
> belief of some great catastrophe; but thus to destroy animals,
> both large and small, in Southern Patagonia, in Brazil, on the
> Cordillera of Peru, in North America, and up to Bering Strait,
> we must shake the entire framework of the globe.[1]

Fossils of unusual creatures have been found in rather hard-to-ex-
plain places. In Australia, New Zealand, Tasmania, and the neigh-
boring islands, fossils are numerous and varied in kind. The *Moa*, a
large wingless bird, similar to the ostrich but much larger in size, has
been found in various places 150 to 250 feet below the surface of the
ground. In other places it is found in caves where the remains of
hundreds and thousands of these gigantic birds are heaped together
in a totally confusing mass. What was it that drove these huge flight-
less birds to higher ground where they perished and were buried
under literally tons of clay, gravel, and other water-transported debris?

Huge dinosaurian fossil graveyards have also been found that
demonstrate the same confusion. What catastrophe could have shaken
the framework of the globe? What could have produced such massive
fossil graveyards?

Index Fossils

In fossil-bearing sedimentary rocks there are often fossils of one
type that are more abundant than others. These fossils serve the geologist as "index fossils." Most of the time the index fossils are marine invertebrates. They are often used to "date" rock layers. If in a
strange formation an index fossil is found, then theoretically it would
be easy to date that particular rock stratum and to correlate it with
other exposures containing similar fossils.

Dr. Morris has listed several examples of fossil communities that
serve as index fossils according to the Geological Time Table:

Periods	Index Fossils
Precambrian:	Algae, bacteria, fungi
Cambrian:	Sponges, snails, jellyfish
Ordovician:	Clams, starfish, worms
Silurian:	Scorpions, corals
Devonian:	Sharks, lungfish
Carboniferous:	Ferns, cockroaches
Permian:	Beetles, dragonflies
Triassic:	Pines, palms
Jurassic:	Crocodiles, turtles
Cretaceous:	Ducks, pelicans
Paleocene:	Rats, hedgehogs
Eocene:	Lemurs, rhinoceroses
Oligocene:	Beavers, squirrels, ants
Miocene:	Camels, wolves
Pliocene:	Horses, elephants
Pleistocene:	Man [2]

While this is certainly not an exhaustive list, it is evident that these animals and plants are basically the same as the living forms today, their extinction in no way proves evolution. But what is unusual is that some of the index fossils believed to have been extinct millions of years ago have somehow managed to show up in recent years as "living fossils." Certainly when this happens their use as index fossils should cease immediately, but this is not always the case.

One notable example of a living fossil is the crossopterygian fish or coelacanth that was believed to be extinct since the Cretaceous Period, about 70 million years ago. This living fossil is about 5½ feet in length and weighs around 180 pounds. It was first discovered in 1938 off the coast of East London in South Africa. A second one was found in 1952 near the Comoro Islands, southwest of Madagascar. Since that time several others have been found in the South Africa and Madagascar areas. The coelacanth possesses seven thick fleshy fins, six of which are inserted on scaly stalks and resemble the limbs of higher vertebrates. But a cross sectional comparison between the coelacanth and a typical reptile has failed to demonstrate a satisfactory correlation between the coelacanth's fins and the reptilian legs.

But the most significant aspect of this living fossil is that according to the evolutionary Geological Time Table, the coelacanth has remained virtually unchanged in all the proposed 70 million years of

The Coelacanth—A "Living Fossil"

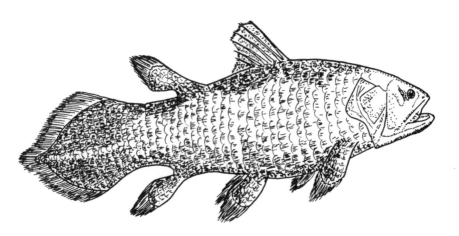

According to the theory of evolution, the coelacanth became extinct seventy million years ago. However, a "living fossil" was found off the coast of Madagascar in the 1930s. Several other have been found since then.
Comparisons of fossil coelacanths with living coelacanths have clearly shown that *no changes* have occurred in this species in over 70 million years!

its existence. There is absolutely no evidence to suggest that the coelacanth was a precursor to modern reptiles. Yet this was the proposal given by evolutionists before the discovery of the living fossil. But if change is a fact and evolution is also a fact, then why hasn't the coelacanth changed in the last 70 million years?

Missing Links?

A paleontologist of a British museum was quoted as saying: "Nine tenths of the talk of evolutionists is sheer nonsense, not founded on observation and unsupported by fact. This museum is full of proofs of the utter falsity of their views. In all this great museum, there is not a particle of evidence of the transmutation of species."

Evolutionists today place great emphasis on fossils as proof of evolution, and many students have been led to believe that just the presence of fossils is sure proof that evolution occurred. But the fossil record does not offer proof of the validity of the theory of evolution.

Evolution must assume that complex life forms came from simple life forms, and therefore it is to be expected that the further back into Earth's history one goes, the less complex the life forms are. Almost every science text contains a Geologic Time Table that traces life on the earth back to the most simple of life forms, the algae and microorganisms. The table assumes that the more complex the life forms, the more recent their appearance in Earth's history. Texts of evolution illustrate the principle of simple to complex in a most precise manner, while in reality such gradations do not always exist in that order. Dr. Walter E. Lammerts has files on over 500 cases in which fossil inversion, the less complex on top of the more complex, actually occurs.[3] He also points out that it is not uncommon to find very complex life forms resting directly on basic granites.

No matter how far evolutionists go back into the fossil record, there are no traces of animal forms which are true intermediates between the various major groups found living today. With the abundance of fossil records available today, evolutionists can no longer hide behind the excuse that the fossil record is incomplete. Since there is not the slightest evidence, either among the living or fossil animals, of any intergrading types following the major groups, it is a fair supposition that there never were any such intergrading types. Dr. T. George has pointed out that the fossil record fails to produce any missing links. He claims that the number of fossils available is "almost unmanageably rich" and that there is no longer need to apologize for the poverty of the fossil record.[4] The rate of discovery of new fossils is outpacing scientists' ability to categorize them. But one thing is clear: the fossil record is mainly composed of evolutionary gaps.

The fossil record seems to suggest that there have never been any missing links. Fossils from even the earliest of rocks can be placed easily into their proper phylum or major group. Animal groups appear to have been "fixed" from the beginning. They do not, according to the fossil record, appear to have ever merged into another animal type. All major phyla, classes, orders and so on, are found in the earliest of fossil-bearing rocks. A star-fish is always a star-fish and an insect is always an insect. Fred J. Meldau believes that "there never were such intermediates . . . these major groups, from the very first, bore the same relation to each other that they do at the present."[5]

Missing links need not be limited to just those gaps that occur between animal or plant groups, but must also refer to the absence of fossils leading up to complex life forms. Fossils in Cambrian rocks show a high degree of development— yet in the Precambrian rocks immediately below the fossil-rich Cambrian rocks, there are no fossils to suggest the gradual evolutionary development leading to complex animals and plants. In other words, according to the fossil record, life appeared suddenly, abundantly, diverse and already complex, just as to be expected in a created world.

Dr. Daniel Axelrod, an evolutionist and professor of botany at the University of California, Davis, sees the absence of Precambrian fossils as a major problem to geology and the theory of evolution:

> One of the major unsolved problems of geology and evolution is the occurrence of diversified, multicellular marine invertebrates of Lower Cambrian rocks and their absence in rocks of greater age. These early Cambrian fossils include porifera, coelenterates, brachiopods, mollusca, echinoids and arthropods. Their high degree of organization clearly indicates that a long period of evolution preceded their appearance in the record. However, when we turn to examine the Precambrian fossils, they are nowhere to be found. Many thick (over 5000 feet) sections of sedimentary rock are now known to lie in unbroken succession below strata containing the earliest Cambrian fossils. These sediments apparently were suitable for the preservation of fossils because they are often identical with overlying rocks which are Fossiliferous yet no fossils are found in them.[6]

It is reported that Dr. Axelrod has evidence of spores of 60 genera of woody plants in Cambrian rocks. The theory of evolution does not have woody plants, such as the conifers, developing until over 200 million years after the Cambrian period. According to the Geological Time Table, no land animals or plants existed during the Cambrian period. Findings such as this must deal a serious blow to the evolutionist who insists life developed through a series of progressive steps leading from the most simple to the most complex. The fossil record reveals extremely complex animals and plants from the very beginning.

Dr. Simpson also admits to the severity of this problem. Just why life should suddenly appear in the Cambrian layers but not in the Precambrian rocks immediately in contact with the Cambrian layers is a mystery unexplainable in terms of the evolutionary theory. Simpson draws attention to this problem in his text, *Life: An Introduction to Biology*:

> The sudden contrast between the Precambrian rocks, in which animal fossils are so rare or dubious, and the Cambrian, in which they are so abundant, poses a serious question: Why? A good scientist must be prepared to say, "I don't know," and that is at present the correct answer.[7]

There seems to be no trace of any animal forms representing intermediate connections (missing links) between the various major groups in the fossil record. Without evidence to prove otherwise, it is not an unfair assumption that there have never been any such intergrading types. *Time Magazine* reports that scientists must "concede that even their most cherished theories are based on embarrassingly few fossil fragments, and that huge gaps exist in the fossil record."[8]

Archaeopteryx—100 percent Bird

Many evolutionists have claimed that *archaeopteryx*, an interesting fossil remains of a bird that not only had claws on its wings, but whose vertebrae extended out along a tail, is a true link between the reptiles and the birds. *Archaeopteryx* is not classified as a 50 percent bird and a 50 percent reptile, but as the oldest known 100 percent bird. Nor is it the only bird with these characteristics. The living *hoactzin* in South America are true birds but also have claws on the leading edges of their wings. *Hoactzin* are considered to be 100 percent birds.

While the "tail" of *archaeopteryx* may be of interest, it is not an indication that it evolved from reptiles any more than the bat's wing indicates that it evolved from a bird or flying insect. Evidence suggests that this is just another variation within the bird family or type.

A recent fossil find has been made of an undoubtedly true bird

A restoration of Archaeopteryx, showing teeth, claws in the wings and a long tail.

that has proved older than the *archaeopteryx* by some 60 million years, according to the evolutionary scale. Dr. James A. Jensen of Brigham Young University has made the assessment that this fossil actually predates *archaeopteryx* and was indeed a "true bird" (see *Science News*, Vol. 112, September 24, 1977, p. 198).

Archaeopteryx has not proved to be a link by any means. Dr. John Ostrom of Yale University, after considering the impact of the newly discovered bird fossil, said: "It is obvious that we must now look for the ancestors of flying birds in a period of time much older than that in which *Archaeopteryx* lived."[9]

Major Gaps Continue to Exist

The fossil record has failed to show a connection between invertebrates and the first fish, or from fish to amphibian, or from amphibian to reptile, or from reptile to bird. The latitudinal variations observed today do not even begin to explain how gills became lungs or scales became feathers. Until evolutionists can produce evidence that ,explains how the gelatinous amphibian egg, designed to develop in an aquatic environment, came to be transformed into the complex amniotic egg of the reptiles, their theory is without solid footing. The fossil record has failed to give support to evolution.

> ... the fossil record does not show a continuous evolutionary progression at all, as the theory requires. The same great gaps between the major kinds of plants and animals that exist in the present world are also found in the fossil world . . . . . . the fossil record speaks not of gradual evolution of life—but of the sudden extinction of life—all over the world, in one age.[10]

To Make a Fossil

Just how do plant and animal parts come to be fossilized? For fossilization to take place, special conditions must exist. Once an animal or plant dies, it must be soon buried in mud or covered with volcanic ash if it is to be preserved. Without this protection, the remains would rapidly perish, leaving no evidence of existence. An animal or plant that dies in a jungle or rain forest will quickly break down into its chemical components and simply disappear. Even solid bone will decompose rather quickly if left exposed to the elements.

The American bison that once roamed the Great Plains in the millions, and died by the millions, has failed to leave fossil evidence of its existence. But the fossil record is not in dire poverty. As already pointed out by Dr. T. George, the fossil record has "become almost unmanageably rich." Nevertheless, it is still composed mainly of gaps between the major life forms.

Fossilization is not occurring anywhere in the world today to the degree necessary to form the gigantic fossil beds known to exist. The Monterey shale in California contains an estimated billion herring that died on four square miles of bay bottom. This evidence suggests some major catastrophic destruction. How did over a billion herring come to be buried at the same time? It has been suggested that the deadly "red tide" may have been responsible for producing the fossilized herring, but red tide does not produce fossils.

In New Mexico a remarkably large dinosaurian graveyard was found. Literally thousands of skeletons were piled on top of one another and interlaced, suggesting that they all died as the result of the same catastrophe. Another dinosaurian graveyard has been found in Wyoming. It has proved to be a veritable mine of dinosaur bones. But the concentration of the fossils indicates that they were piled up like a log jam. The same kind of finds have been made in Alberta. Huge graveyards of dinosaur skeletons piled together as the result of some catastrophic event. In Belgium is an even more amazing dinosaurian graveyard. Its vertical extension is through more than a hundred feet of rock!

Similar dinosaurian graveyards have been found on every continent. What large-scale catastrophic event could have produced such huge piles of skeletal remains? Also, why are fossilized skeletons of "modern" animals often found just as abundantly and sometimes in the same graveyards with those of supposedly more ancient animals?

There are no natural phenomena taking place today capable of forming the huge sedimentary rock beds that were formed at one time in the past. Sedimentary rock layers are known to extend several miles in depth, length, and width. In Glacier National Park is a Precambrian limestone strata that measures some 350 miles long, 35 miles wide, and several thousands of feet thick. It is said to be nearly a billion years old. But even more puzzling is that this Precambrian limestone is resting on top of Cretaceous shales that are said to be much younger. How could such a huge structure of greater age come to rest on top of a much younger rock layer? The "trust-fault" hypothesis which suggests that folding and bending of the earth's crust would be sufficient to move the estimated "eight hundred thousand billion tons" of Precambrian limestone a minimum distance of 35 miles eventually to rest on top of the younger Cretaceous shales is utterly ridiculous.

The Present: Key to the Past?

There are many who believe that the present is the key to the past. This is called the *doctrine of uniformitarianism.* But it is incapable of explaining such phenomena as those found at Glacier National Park. Evolution is often closely associated with the uniformitarian doctrine by the fact that both require an immensity of time.

> . . . the Scottish geologist, James Hutton . . . maintained that the present is the key to the past and that, given sufficient time, processes now at work could account for all the geologic features of the Globe. This philosophy, which came to be known as the doctrine of uniformitarianism, demands an immensity of time; it has now gained universal acceptance among intelligent and informed people.[11]

There are simply too many geologic formations in existence that uniformitarianism cannot explain. The processes occurring today cannot explain how some of the earth's geologic features were formed. Igneous rocks were supposedly formed by the upwelling of magmas from deep within the earth's mantle. But there is no process occurring today that can account for the huge igneous batholiths and laccoliths that are presently with us. The Columbia Plateau of the northwestern United States is a tremendous lava plateau of almost incredible thickness (several thousand feet) and covers almost 200,000 square miles. Modern volcanism is meaningless when compared to such a structure as this. We know of no modern process that could form such a gigantic structure.

The process by which metamorphic rocks were converted from sedimentary rocks (e.g., limestone into marble) does not seem to be taking place today. Sedimentary rocks not only cover most of the earth's surface but also contain fossils. Uniformitarianism has not been able to demonstrate any process today that is capable of forming the huge sedimentary rock layers throughout the world. The Saint Peter Sandstone and its correlative formations cover practically all of the United States from California to Vermont and from Canada to Tennessee. Only a continental flood could have accomplished such a vast sedimentary deposit—a flood that would have been felt throughout the world.

We are told that coal beds were formed during the Carboniferous period around 300 million years ago. Evolutionists relying on uniformitarianism claim that coal was formed as huge fields of plant remains decayed, accumulated, and compacted. These peat bogs eventually turned into coal. However, there are huge peat bogs throughout Florida today, but there is not a single piece of evidence that any of these bogs are in the process of producing coal. In addition, coal seams are often found in strata with shale, limestone, or sandstone, and sometimes the strata are repeated dozens of times in vertical sections.

Fossilized tree trunks that extend through several strata (polystrata) of coal and other rock layers are often found in coal beds, speaking loudly of the impossibility that coal beds were formed by a process requiring millions of years. In the Coal Measures at Blackrod near Wigan in Lancashire is a polystrata tree trunk that was preserved as a cast that measures some 38 vertical feet! For such a cast to have formed, the original tree must have been surrounded and buried by sediment which was compacted before the major portion of the tree decomposed. This could only have happened if sedimentation occurred rapidly.

Similar finds have been made elsewhere, suggesting that the huge coal beds were deposited rapidly, not over millions of years as suggested by the theory of evolution. Only a flood of gigantic proportions could have formed such coal beds. Fossilized trees are sometimes found in coal beds lying at an angle or even upside down! Most certainly this speaks of rapid deposition by flood waters. Coal seams sometimes are split by transported marine sediments, and marine fossils are often found in coal beds—further evidence of massive flooding.

Many coal seams have no sign of a fossil soil under them. This is not consistent with the belief that coal beds were formed by the gradual accretion of humus. It is not uncommon to find boulders, some quite large, in coal seams. The evidence seems to favor coal formation by a gigantic flood rather than the slow accumulation of vegetative matter over an immense period of time.

The presently accepted evolutionary method of explaining the formation of coal beds is inadequate and cannot account for the presence of polystrata tree trunks, the presence of marine deposits, or the presence of large boulders. But in the light of the evidence, a catastrophic flood theory appears to be far more likely. To reject the flood theory because it is not consistent with the doctrine of uniformitarianism would also require that one simply overlook available evidence.

Problems with Petrified Forests

Petrified forests are found in many parts of the world; the area near

Cairo, Egypt has a well-known fossil forest. There are large fossil tree trunks in Napa Valley, California, as well as the much-visited Petrified Forest in Arizona. The Yellowstone National Park has several areas containing petrified trees. One of these areas covers almost 35,000 acres. A petrified redwood trunk with a diameter of about ten feet has been found in this region. This is one of the largest fossil trees found.

The exact process of petrification is not fully understood, but it is believed that the matrix in which the trees in the Yellowstone area are entombed points to volcanic activity as well as to the action of water. The manner in which the trees are lying around points out that they were water-transported and deposited in a manner not unlike a log drift left stranded by receding waters.

Along with the remains of these trees is fossil evidence of other plants; ferns, horsetails, broad-leaved banana-like plants, magnolias, and grapes. Well over 100 different plant fossils have been identified in the Yellowstone Park, many of which no longer grow in that latitude or elevation. The problem—how did they get there?

A Very Big Problem

In the frozen wastelands of Siberia and Alaska are the remains of an estimated five million mammoths. Mammoths are among the most abundant of fossil remains. In some cases the entire body has been found perfectly preserved in ice. The huge, lumbering beasts were closely related to present day elephants but much larger. Some mammoths measured more than 14 feet high at the shoulder. Many had tusks that curved down from the upper jaw, then curved up and crossed in front of the trunk. The tusks measured some 13 feet in length! Certain types of mammoths were covered with long hair that some scientists believed served as protection against the extreme cold of the northern climates. There is evidence, however, that the northern climate may not have been very cold when the mammoths existed.

The mere presence of these beasts in such vast numbers has led to serious questions concerning the study of ancient climates. That mammoths could have survived in a land where today, during the height of the Artic summer, plants will seldom grow larger than a few inches high, presents an obvious problem. These creatures needed

The Mammoth, an extinct elephant, has left abundant fossil remains in the Siberian wastelands. So abundant has been the ivory from these mammoth fossil deposits that seventeenth and eighteenth century piano keys in Europe were more often than not made from mammoth ivory rather than from African ivory.

somewhere around 500 to 600 pounds of vegetation daily just to maintain the food requirements for their enormous bodies. There is no way that the present northern wastelands could provide the necessary vegetation—even in the summer at the peak of the growing season—to feed the numerous mammoth herds that once roamed there. Yet they are often pictured as having lived in a cold and snowy climate. This simply cannot be.

The problem becomes more complicated as one goes further north, where the mammoth fossils only become more numerous. How could they have survived in such a desolate land completely covered with snow and ice? What did they feed on?

The doctrine of uniformitarianism is utterly hopeless in attempting to explain the presence of the mammoth fossils. Evolutionists may be able to place the mammoths on a Geologic Time Table, but they cannot explain their presence in northern Siberia.

The presence of the mammoth fossils has been known for some time. Both Lyell and Darwin were aware of the frozen mammoths. They presented such a threat to Lyell's theory that he vainly attempted to explain them away by suggesting they were "caught in a cold snap while swimming." Darwin simply admitted that he saw no logical explanation for the presence of these huge frozen creatures. According to Digby, an English explorer of Siberia prior to World War I, there are some 25 locations in Siberia where these quick-frozen mammoths may be found.

Many of the mammoths found with the whole body intact were found in an upright or kneeling position, some with foliage in their mouths and stomachs. The foliage is characteristic only of a temperate to subtropical climate zone.

There is no known process today that can account for the quick-freezing of an animal weighing several tons. Donald E. Patten explains that dogs can endure temperatures around -90°F. for hours and not freeze. The evidence is that mammoths were not just frozen; they were quick-frozen before they even had time to swallow the food in their mouths! The type of plants in the mouths and stomachs of the mammoths suggest a temperate to subtropical climate at the time the quick-freezing took place.

Patten has suggested that the huge beasts actually died of asphyxiation as evidenced by the concentration of blood found in their heads:

> The mammoths are found, not underfed as if their diet were lichens and willows. Rather they are found, marbled in fat, apparently in the midst of their last delectable dinner, a choice selection of luxuriant herbs. The concentration of blood found in their heads is a strong indicator that they were asphyxiated . . . Sanderson claims that tests have been made, blood-typing these ancient beasts, and in a study of their tissue, a determination of the temperatures surrounding their demise may be ascertained. This is because when an animal dies, water begins to separate within its cells. When it freezes, all separation ceases. The modest amount of water separation in the cells drove Sand-

erson to the conclusion that temperatures surrounding their demise may have been -150°F. and perhaps lower. This is unearthly cold.[12]

The quick-frozen mammoths are found in an area that is central to the geographical pole. There is no evidence that this region was glaciated by an ice mass. Mammoths not located in this central geographical pole area did not give evidence of having been quick-frozen, but rather quickly drowned and just as quickly buried.

Other evidence of a sudden and extreme drop in temperature in this northern Siberian region is that sedges, beans, grasses, and buttercups are found in full growth, also quick-frozen. These plants often were found bearing seeds. A quick-frozen elderberry tree was found laden with ripe berries! The suggestion that a slow-moving ice mass of the Ice Age overtook the mammoths and various fruit-ripened plant life is ludicrous. Uniformitarian theories are of no benefit in suggesting a possible explanation for this unique situation.

Footprints in Stone Don't Lie

According to the Geologic Time Table, the last of the dinosaurs became extinct about 70 million years ago. Dinosaur fossils have become useful index fossils for the paleontologist. It is believed that certain types of dinosaurs, some of which were unbelievably large, lived at various times and therefore serve as index fossils for determining the age of certain sedimentary rock strata. According to the evolutionist, these creatures died out millions of years before man came on the scene.

Dinosaur footprints have been bound in abundance in rocks in many places in the world, and occasionally human footprints have been found in the same rock with the dinosaurian prints. This certainly cannot be, according to the Geologic Time Table—unless the table is in complete error. Nevertheless, evidence of the coexistence of dinosaurs and man has been known for many years. There are many places where dinosaurs are depicted on cave and canyon walls. In the 1930s, in the limestone beds of the Puluxy River in the Cretaceous Glen Rose formation of central Texas, footprints of both dinosaur and man were discovered to exist in the same rock layer—at the same geologic level! In two cases, the two types of footprints

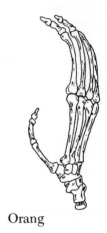
Orang

Man

The uniqueness of the human foot is clearly seen in this top view of the right foot of an orang and the right foot of a man. The orang has a strongly handlike foot with long side toes, small great toe and a small heel and ankle region (tarsus). Man has a large tarsus and weight-bearing surface, and a great toe with shortened side toes.

actually overlap each other. Dr. Morris claims that many of these are in distinct trails—right foot, left foot, right foot and so on. These prints could only have been made by a human.

The most distinguishable feature of man that separates him from ape-like creatures is not his brain or hand—but his *foot*! The foot of man is unique and easily distinguishable from that of an ape (see diagram).

In many cases, legends are based on truth. Where did the legends dealing with huge "dragons" come from? Several civilizations have left records of huge beasts. It is very possible that these legends came from beasts actually seen—dinosaurs!

Job, one of the oldest patriarchs of the Old Testament, records the presence of two rather large creatures that existed in his lifetime. The first beast is called *Behemoth*:

> Behold now behemoth, which I made with thee; he eateth grass as an ox.
> Lo, now, his strength is in his loins, and his force is in the muscles of his belly.

He moveth his tail like a cedar; the sinews of his thighs are knit together.

His bones are like strong pieces of bronze; his bones are like bars of iron.

He is the chief of the ways of God; he who made him can make his sword to approach unto him.

Surely the mountains bring him forth food, where all the beasts of the field play.

He lieth under the shady trees, in the covert of the reed, and fens.

The shady trees cover him with their shadow; the willows of the brook compass him about.

Behold, he drinketh up a river, and hasteneth not; he trusteth that he can draw up Jordan into his mouth.

He taketh it with his eyes; his nose pierceth through snares.

Job 40:15–24

A feeble attempt has been made to explain that Behemoth may be a hippopotamus. But the hippopotamus is not characterized by the strength in its thighs, and its tail certainly does not resemble a cedar tree as does the tail of Behemoth. Hippopotami are large but not the size indicated in Job's description. Behemoth appears so large that he "can draw up the Jordan into his mouth." From the description given by Job, the only acceptable alternative is that Behemoth was a huge dinosaur, maybe even Brontosarus himself.

Job gives an even lengthier description of a second beast, *Leviathan*:

Canst thou draw out leviathan with an hook, or his tongue with a cord which thou lettest down? Canst thou put an hook into his nose, or bore his jaw through with a thorn?

Will he make many supplications unto thee? Will he speak soft words unto thee? . . .

Canst thou fill his skin with barbed irons, or his head with fish spears?

Lay thine hand upon him, remember the battle, do no more . . .

None is so fierce that dares stir him up; who then is able to stand before me? . . .

Who can open the doors of his face? His teeth are terrible round about.

His scales are his pride, shut up together as with a close seal.

One is so near to another, that no air can come between them.

They are joined one to another, they stick together, that they cannot be sundered.

By his sneezings a light doth shine, and his eyes are like the eyelids of the morning.

Out of his mouth go burning lamps, and sparks of fire leap out. Out of his nostril goeth smoke, as out of a boiling pot or caldron. His breath kindleth coals, and a flame goeth out of his mouth.

In his neck remaineth strength, and sorrow is turned into joy before him.

The flakes of his flesh are joined together; they are firm in themselves; they cannot be moved . . .

The sword of him that layeth at him cannot hold: the spear, the dart, nor the javelin.

He esteemeth iron as straw, and bronze as rotten wood.

The arrow cannot make him flee, slingstones are turned with him into stubble.

Sharp stones are under him; he spreadeth sharp pointed things upon the mire.

He maketh the deep to boil like a pot; he maketh the sea like a pot of ointment.

Job 41:1–3, 7–8, 10, 14–23, 26–31

Some have suggested that Leviathan may be a crocodile or alligator, but I do not think so. The alligator may attain a length of nearly 20 feet, but this is not Leviathan. In the 104th Psalm, King David records that Leviathan is also found in the great and wide sea, the Mediterranean.

The evidence suggests that our thinking about the antiquity of dinosaurs must change, for it indicates that man and dinosaurs were at one time contemporaries! The huge dragon lizards that still live on the small Indonesian Island of Komodo are certainly living representatives of the dinosaurs.

Only about 500 years ago the *aepyornis*, a dinosaur bird over 10 feet tall and weighing 1,000 pounds, still lived on the island of Madagascar. If the *aepyornis* had not actually been observed at that time, the paleontologist would most likely have incorrectly placed it somewhere on the Geologic Time Table has having become extinct several million years ago.

Trilobites

Trilobites, which are among the oldest known fossils, also serve as important index fossils for the paleontologist, especially when the reference is being made for the Cambrian, Ordovician, Silurian and Devonian periods. They are often used by geologists to determine relative ages of some of the oldest fossiliferous formations. Evidence suggesting that trilobites may be of more recent times would also be sure reason to invalidate any theory of evolution concerning them. There may be just such evidence.

As with other Cambrian fossils, trilobites are found fully developed and already complex arthropods. No rock of an earlier age has yielded an intermediate stage of trilobite development. They seem to appear suddenly without any evidence of a precursory type. Evolutionists know that trilobites are among the oldest fossils but are unable to explain why they suddenly appear, fully developed, without evidence of gradual, intermediate forms to support the evolutionary hypothesis concerning their origin.

A very remarkable find was made on June 1, 1968, that may completely upset the theory of evolution. Mr. William J. Meister, Sr., a drafting supervisor and amateur rockhound, was looking for trilobites in the well-known "trilobite beds" of Antelope Springs, about 43 miles northwest of Delta, Utah. About half way up a 2,000-foot, fairly steep mountain face, Meister broke off a large slab of rock that turned out to be the footprint of a human wearing sandals that had trilobites right in the footprint itself!

> . . . I broke off a large, approximately two-inch thick slab of rock. Upon hitting it on the edge with my hammer, it fell open like a book. To my great astonishment I saw on one side the footprint of a human *with trilobites right in the footprint itself.* The other half of the rock slab showed an almost perfect mold of the footprint and fossils. Amazingly the human was wearing a sandal![13]

Additional finds of human footprints in this area have been made by Dean Bitter, an educator in the public schools of Salt Lake City, and by Dr. Burdick, a well-traveled consulting geologist of Tucson, Arizona. Another consulting geologist verified that the area from which the fossil sandal with the trilobites attached was at one time a shore environment believed to have existed during the Cambrian period, 500–600 million years ago!

The most apparent questions are: Just what are human footprints doing in Cambrian rock, and How did trilobites end up on the bottom of a sandal? The geological time scale would place trilobites in the Cambrian period, but these small marine arthropods are believed to have become extinct around the Devonian period no less than 350 million years ago. These particular trilobites are associated with Cambrian rocks and therefore suggest an even earlier age of some 500–600 million years. This would also suggest that the human with the sandal would also be some 500–600 million years old. Much more likely, however, is the logical explanation that neither are 500–600 million years of age but of much more recent times.

Meister was unable to get a single geologist at the University of Utah to look at his remarkable find. From just a single tooth, evolutionists are willing to attempt to construct not only the complete skeleton of its owner, but also suggest its eating habits and the type of environment in which it lived. Some evolutionists become excited over very small fragmentary skeletal parts. One certainly would think that a find of the magnitude of Meister's would have brought out true scientifically minded individuals by the scores, but instead it was met with a quiet hush as though it were some kind of embarrassment to the scientific community.

Case of the Slow Bat?

It is generally taught that the formation of stalactites and stalagmites in caves is the result of an incredibly slow accretion process. This accretion-type growth requires multiples of thousands of years just to add inches to the stalactite and corresponding stalagmite. However, in a *National Geographic Magazine* article entitled "Carlsbad Caverns in Color" by Robert Harris (October, 1953), is a photograph of a bat entombed in a stalagmite. The evidence suggests that the bat was entombed so quickly that neither bacterial decay nor predators had an opportunity to destroy it. This stalagmite casts doubts on the theory that stalagmite growth is always incredibly slow. Or maybe bats are much slower than we realize. Maybe the doctrine of uniformitarianism should have been buried with that bat.

The fossil record fails to provide the kind of evidence evolutionists insist is there to support their theories. On the contrary, the fossil record demonstrates the sudden demise of life. It shows evidence of flooding of unbelievable dimensions.

Skeletal remains are found piled upon one another in the same manner as would a log jam left by receding flood waters. In some cases dinosaur skeletons are found in piles that may be hundreds of feet thick vertically. Sedimentary rock layers thousands of feet thick and hundreds of miles in length and width give further evidence that there was, at one time, a flood of gigantic proportions.

The earth's huge coal beds suggest rapid deposition of plant material by flood transportation, not by the slow accretion of plant material as suggested by the doctrine of uniformitarianism. Large boulders and marine fossils, as well as fossilized tree trunks found in coal seams in upright and even upside-down position, could only be the result of flooding.

I am convinced that there is strong evidence to suggest that a global flood occurred— the Genesis Flood of the Old Testament. Such a flood can account for many of the geological formations that remain only a mystery to present uniformitarian hypotheses. I also understand the consequences that would occur if the Genesis Flood were accepted in the scientific community—the theory of evolution would be utterly destroyed.

8. DETERMINING THE AGE OF A FOSSIL

Just how do geologists and paleontologists determine the age of a fossil? How can they be certain that a given fossil lived 500 million years ago? Are there instruments of science that can accurately determine dates as to when an organism lived? Many evolutionists tend to convey the impression that there are such instruments. It appears they would have the general public believe that these instruments produce accurate readings as to the antiquity of a given fossil. But, in actuality, a fossil is dated by the rock layer in which it is found. The rock layer is dated, in turn, by the fossil content. *Circular reasoning?*

Long before radioactive dating methods were conceived, the assumption was made that evolution always moved in an uphill direction, from the simple to the complex. It was then an easy task to arrange a scale that showed how this uphill development took place. Simple life forms were placed at the bottom of the scale, and the more complex life forms were placed near the top. Extinct life forms were placed in the middle of the scale so that the simple would always be below the complex. In time, this scale developed into the Geologic Time Table and is now commonly found in science textbooks.

Even though there are numerous exceptions, it is assumed that the lower the rock stratum, the older it is. The younger rocks are always near the top of the stratum. Within each rock stratum there may be certain fossils that seem to be characteristically abundant. These fossils are known as "index fossils". With this system, a reference may be made to the Geologic Time Table and the fossil may be located or placed so that it is between a similar type—always so that the simpler is below the more complex.

Estimates are made (though not based on actual observations) as to how long it took one life form to develop into a higher form, and then an assumed date is placed on the Geologic Table. The key to the whole process of dating a rock or a fossil is, therefore, based upon the assumption that the theory of evolution is a fact.

Radiological Dating

Have the more recently developed radioactive methods improved the reliability of dating rocks or fossils? Some think so; others are not sure. There have been no major changes in the Geologic Time Table as a result of radiometric dating methods. As a matter of fact, many of these instruments produce such varied results that scientists are often forced to refer to the Geologic Time Table to know which "date" is correct. The Time Table that the radiometric dating methods are supposed to verify are in turn verified by the Time Table.

Are radiometric dating methods accurate? Consider the following example. A volcanic rock known to have been formed in 1801 near Hualalei, Hawaii, gave potassium-argon readings that varied from 160 million years to almost three billion years! The rock was actually less than 200 years old. In another case, carbon-14, considered by many to be very accurate, showed the shells of *living* mollusks to be over 2,000 years old!

There is no way to verify the readings of radiometric instruments except by reference to the evolutionary-based Geologic Time Table. This can hardly be considered as a scientifically accurate method for dating fossils.

Carbon-14

Carbon-14 dating is the most widely known of all the radiometric methods of dating fossils. This method, developed by Dr. Frank W. Libby in 1947, held great promise for many evolutionists who believed that they now had an accurate instrument for dating fossils back to at least 50,000 years. But carbon-14 dating has been found to contain too many uncertainties.

The formation of carbon-14 begins at the sun. Every star—and our sun is certainly a star—sends out particles along with light and heat energy. Some of these particles, traveling at the speed of light (186,000 miles per second), are positively charged nuclei of hydrogen atoms called "primary cosmic rays" or "protons." The electrons have been stripped away from the hydrogen atom, leaving only the single positively charged proton.

When this primary cosmic particle strikes the upper regions of the earth's atmosphere at about 30,000 to 50,000 feet, it still possesses sufficient energy to break up nitrogen and oxygen atoms. This atomic breakup releases neutrons (neutrally charged atomic particles) that frequently transmute nitrogen into carbon which would now have a mass of 14 as compared to normal carbon with a mass of 12; a 16½ percent increase in weight. Carbon-14 is radioactive and therefore unstable. It spontaneously begins to convert to nitrogen and has a half-life of somewhere between 5,568 to 5,760 years. This means that in 5,568 to 5,760 years, only 50 percent of the original carbon-14 will still be present; twice this period will leave only 25 percent of the original carbon-14; three times this period will leave only 12.5 percent of the original carbon-14; and so on.

Approximately 22 pounds of carbon-14 are produced in the atmosphere each year. Carbon-14 is oxidized to carbon dioxide (CO_2) and mixed throughout the atmosphere by air currents and then utilized by photosynthetic plants along with nonradioactive CO_2 to form carbohydrates. Most of the CO_2 is absorbed into oceans due to the high solubility of carbon dioxide in water. In either case, the CO_2 has now entered the earth's carbon cycle to be utilized ultimately by *all* living things. The radioactive carbon-14 may then be found uniformly in all living organisms.

Once an organism dies, be it plant or animal, the uniform absorption of carbon-14 ceases. Carbon-14 now begins to change back into nitrogen at a measurable and steady rate. Therefore, if the half-life of carbon-14 is at the upper limits, say 5,700 years, then a fossil showing only 50 percent of the carbon-14 present in living organisms would be 5,700 years old; if it has only 25 percent of the carbon-14 within a living organism, then it would be 11,400 years, and so on. Measurements of radioactive carbon in fossils do not yield actual dates but only the amount of carbon-14 in the sample. Dates are the interpretations based on the carbon-14 quantity within the sample.

It would be a very simple matter to determine the age of a fossil at the time of its death by using the carbon-14 method of dating, provided certain other conditions exist:

1. There can be no seepage of water or any other element that would add carbon-14 to the specimen. If this has happened, then any date determined by radiometric dating would be invalidated.

FORMATION OF RADIOACTIVE CARBON-14

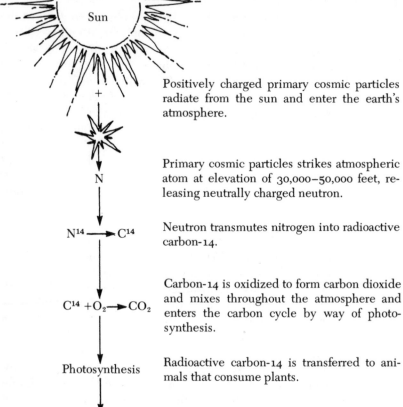

Sun

+

N

$N^{14} \longrightarrow C^{14}$

$C^{14} + O_2 \longrightarrow CO_2$

Photosynthesis

Death

Positively charged primary cosmic particles radiate from the sun and enter the earth's atmosphere.

Primary cosmic particles strikes atmospheric atom at elevation of 30,000–50,000 feet, releasing neutrally charged neutron.

Neutron transmutes nitrogen into radioactive carbon-14.

Carbon-14 is oxidized to form carbon dioxide and mixes throughout the atmosphere and enters the carbon cycle by way of photosynthesis.

Radioactive carbon-14 is transferred to animals that consume plants.

Carbon-14 begins to decay with the death of the organism: 5700 years = 50% of C^{14}
11,400 years = 25% of C^{14}
17,100 years = 12.5% of C^{14}

How can the geologist or paleontologist be certain that in the long years of the existence of a given fossil this situation has never occurred?

2. The fraction of carbon-14 that the organism possessed at the time of its death must be known. It is assumed that the vegetative matter of the earth was the same in the past as it is today. But considerable evidence suggests that at some time in the past there was a global subtropical climate and very likely a greater land surface to water surface ratio than at present. Organisms living during this time

would be exposed to a much smaller amount of carbon-14 and their remains would obviously contain very little, if any, radioactive carbon.

3. Perhaps most important of all is the fact that carbon-14 is presently building up in the atmosphere. The use of carbon-14 is based on the assumption that it is in equilibrium or steady state in the atmosphere. That is, the overall rate of carbon-14 formation in the atmosphere is equal to its rate of decay.

However, by direct and measurable observations, evidence shows that carbon-14 is still building up in the atmosphere and is not in equilibrium. The rate of decay has been measured and found to be only about two thirds as great as the rate of formation.[1] It is generally agreed that it would have taken only 30,000 years for carbon-14 to reach a state of equilibrium. The fact that these two rates, formation and decay, are not in equilibrium suggests that the earth's atmosphere is not yet 30,000 years old!

The amount of carbon-14 presently in the atmosphere would have been formed in only 10,000 years. This presents a very serious problem for the evolutionist who would insist that the earth's atmosphere is billions of years old.

Libby was aware of this unbalanced state of carbon-14 in the atmosphere, "but discounted the evidence in favor of what he took to be more compelling, albeit hearsay, evidence that the earth is too old for carbon-14 to be out of balance."[2]

Libby found the rate of decay (R_d) to be 15.3 counts per gram per minute for radioactive carbon from the living biosphere and the rate of formation (R_f) to be 18.8 counts per gram per minute. This would give a ratio of: $R = R_d/R_f = .81$. More recent finds have placed the ratio as follows:

$$R = {}^{13.3}/_{18.4} = .72$$

The more recent data suggest that the atmosphere is even younger than Libby's calculations. A state of equilibrium would yield a ratio of 1.0, not .72!

All calculations made by carbon-14 should either use the observed ratio of .72 instead of the assumed 1.0, or the carbon-14 dating method should be abandoned. A value of .72 for the ratio between the rate of formation and the rate of decay would bring all carbon-14 dated samples to 10,000 years or less. And yet, with the knowledge that carbon-14 dates have not been adjusted to compensate for the known error, scientists still are content to use the misleading dates produced by this now questionable radiometric dating method.

Radiocarbon (C¹⁴) in Biosphere

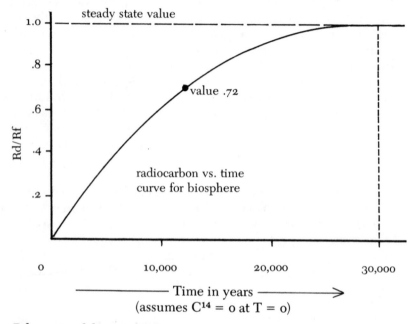

Rd = rate of decay of C¹⁴
Rf = rate of formation of C¹⁴

Radiocarbon would reach steady state in only 30,000 years. Present measurements of rate of formation in ratio to rate of decay indicates the earth's atmosphere is only around 10,000 years old.

Uranium-Lead Ratio

Carbon-14 dates can only apply to organic fossils. In order for carbon-14 to be absorbed into the organism, the organism must be capable of participating in the carbon cycle. Inorganic rocks and minerals do not participate in the carbon cycle and, cannot absorb carbon or carbon-14. Geologists have turned to another radioactive dating method to obtain ages of inorganic rocks—the uranium-lead ratio.

In 1907, Dr. Boltwood developed a dating method based on radio-active uranium. Uranium is known to undergo natural radioactive decay with lead as the end product of its disintegration. It is believed to yield a half-life of 4.5 billion years. By comparing the ratio of uranium to the amount of lead, ratios can be turned into ages, thereby giving "dates" to rock layers that contain uranium.

Dr. Simpson believes that uranium-lead dating holds great promise in helping the geologist ascertain ages for uranium-bearing rocks. He lists the formula used but does not mention the problems associated with this dating method.

> When a mineral containing a radioactive element, uranium, for example, first crystallizes, it includes none of the products of radioactive transformation of that element. Such products then start to accumulate at a constant rate.[3]

That none of the lead products of radioactive uranium decay were present when the uranium was first formed is only an assumption that cannot be proved and is not necessarily so. The formula used by geologists who employ the uranium-lead dating method is, in very simple form, like this:

$$\frac{\text{Grams of lead}}{\text{Grams of uranium}} \times 7{,}600{,}000{,}000 = \text{Age in years}$$

What seemed to be a very simple process just a few years ago may not be so simple after all. Lead may be produced by more than one process. Uranium-238 breaks down into lead-206 in an estimated half-life of 4.5 billion years. But uranium-235 will also break down into lead-207 in a half-life of only 0.7 billion years, whereas thorium-232 will also produce lead-208 in a half-life believed to be 14.1 billion years. Geologists now find that they are working with radiogenic lead from three sources, not just one. In addition to this, common lead-204 is often found in association with the three radiogenic lead isotopes. At this point it becomes an almost unbelievably difficult if not impossible task to separate the four types of lead from each other in order to determine which one was produced by what process of decay.

Uranium is easily washed out of the uranium system by ground-water and therefore may move in and out of the system. If this has happened—and there is no way of knowing it hasn't—then the uranium-lead method is practically meaningless. One can never be sure if part of the component of the ratio has been washed out or added, thereby yielding inaccurate dates.

Furthermore, there is no way of knowing how much nonradiogenic lead was originally in the mineral. Without this information, the uranium-lead ratio means little scientifically. If you don't know how much lead was in the original mineral, how can the present amount be meaningful? There is simply no way of knowing whether all the lead present, or just a part of it, was produced by uranium decay.

Potassium-Argon

The potassium-argon ratio method of dating rocks was developed by Aldrich and Nier in 1948. While it holds greater promise than the uranium-lead method, it is plagued by some of the same problems. Potassium is found in most igneous and some sedimentary rocks and therefore has a much wider use than does uranium-lead methods. Radioactive potassium (K-40) decays to produce radiogenic argon (A-40) in an estimated half-life of 1.3 billion years.

Potassium-argon ratios have produced greatly varying dates on the same sample. As already mentioned, volcanic rock in Hawaii from a known eruption in 1801 was "dated" by the potassium-argon method which produced dates varying from 160 million years to three billion years of age.

In addition to the varying dates, the half-life of 1.3 billion years for radioactive potassium-40 is far from being settled. Decay constants for potassium are still not certain. Radiogenic argon-40 may easily be contaminated by atmospheric argon-40. Since argon is a gas, it can move easily in and out of potassium-bearing minerals, and there is no way of knowing just how much non-radiogenic argon-40 was in the original potassium source.

Other radiological clocks have not proved any more successful than these mentioned. But the most significant observation about radiological clocks is that they have not made any major changes in the Geologic Time Table. Rocks are still dated by their fossil content and the fossils are dated by their assumed position on the evolutionary history of life. The evolutionists are back to where they started; the greatest proof for evolution is the assumption that it could have happened. Once this assumption is made, it becomes a rather easy matter for one to arrange a chart going from simple to complex. The chart then becomes the "key" in dating fossils.

RADIOLOGICAL CLOCKS

Method	Concept	Developer	Disadvantages
Uranium-lead ratio	Uranium undergoes decay with lead as the end product. The ratio of U/Pb will give the age of the mineral	Boltwood 1907	1. No way of knowing how much non-radiogenic lead in original state. 2. Lead is end product of three different radio-series
Potassium-argon ratio	(88% of time) $K^{40} \rightarrow Ca^{40}$ (11% of time) $K^{40} \rightarrow A^{40}$ therefore, $\dfrac{K^{40}}{A^{40}} = Age$	Aldrich & Nier 1948	1. Contamination of radiogenic A^{40} by atmospheric A^{40} 2. Decay Constants still somewhat uncertain 3. Argon leakage
Rubidium-strontium ratio	$Rb^{87} \rightarrow Sr^{87}$ (half-life of Rb^{87} approx. 6×10^9 yrs) $\dfrac{Sr^{87}}{Rb^{87}} = Age$	Hans & Walling 1938	1. Half-life of Rb not certain 2. Rb is rare element (K:Rb = 80:1) 3. Isotopic composition of common Sr variable
Carbon-14	$N^{14} \rightarrow C^{14}$ by neutron impact caused by cosmic radiation. Half-life approx. 5700 years.	Libby 1947	1. Is cosmic radiation constant 2. The formation and decay of C-14 not in equilibrium 3. Subject to contamination by water seepage.

9. POSSIBLE CAUSES OF MASS EXTINCTION

The fossil record clearly indicates that many life forms were eradicated suddenly. Dinosaurs disappeared as did the trilobites, mammoths and mastodons, saber-toothed cat, ground sloth, and many others. Their fossil graveyards indicate that they were suddenly and violently destroyed, their remains often deposited in huge piles with unrelated species. What could have caused such destruction?

Dr. Norman D. Newell, curator of the Department of Fossil Invertebrates at the American Museum of Natural History in New York and professor of invertebrate paleontology at Columbia University, believes this mass extinction constitutes a major problem for the evolutionist.[1]

Roughly 2,500 families of animals can be found only in the fossil record. Local disasters such as volcanic eruptions are inadequate explanations; whatever the catastrophe, it had to be on such a large scale as to affect the entire globe. Many explanations have been attempted, but none, outside the Genesis Flood, has satisfactorily explained the cause for the mass extinction of these animals.

Competition for Food

It is commonly taught that dinosaurs became extinct with the evolution of mammals that proved to be more successful food competitors. Darwin believed the wide variation among animal groups was brought about by competition for food. Many people believe that as the food supply became reduced, the dinosaurs were faced with extinction. There are several reasons, however, to suggest that this may not have been the case. Dr. Newell points out that extinction came not just to the dinosaurs but simultaneously to many other unrelated life forms as well. While it may be tempting to conclude that food competition led to the extinction of the dinosaurs, it fails to explain the equally impressive and simultaneous extinction in the sea of the ammonite mollusks.

Too Specialized

It has also been proposed that certain animals became so "specialized" in their lifestyle that any minor change in the environment would be sufficient to cause their demise. Only those that were "unspecialized" were able to survive the environmental changes. But there are too many exceptions. Dr. Newell explained in a lecture given at the University of Michigan in 1962 that this line of reasoning is not consistent with what is observed. He pointed out that many of the species that became extinct were no more specialized than some groups that survived.

The Ice Age

Many have theorized that the encroaching glaciers of the Ice Age caused mass extinction. But, as pointed out by Dr. Newell, none of the extinctions coincided with glacial advances. In addition, the glaciers did not reach the equatorial latitudes where mass extinction also took place. The significant point is that many characteristic groups—dinosaurs, marine reptiles, flying reptiles, ammonite mollusks, bottom-dwelling aquatic mollusks, as well as many kinds of marine plankton, were represented by world-wide distribution. Yet evidence suggests that they disappeared throughout the world at about the same time.

Hunted by Man

A large number of investigators have proposed that the large mammals were possibly hunted to extinction by prehistoric man. It is suggested that fire may have been used as a weapon. It is also pointed out that the mass extinctions coincided with the rapid development of agriculture. The major objection to this theory is that before this stage of agricultural development, a mass extinction of game would have produced a mass extinction of the hunter as well.

Even though it is unlikely that prehistoric man caused the demise of the large mammals, such an explanation would still not explain how the remains of these animals came to be buried by hundreds of feet of sedimentary rock.

Pathogenic Organisms

Dr. Newell makes the suggestion that the extinction of the dinosaurs may have been the result of a great increase in atmospheric oxygen and an alternatively explosive evolution of pathogenic fungi. But he admits that while pathogenic organisms might destroy large numbers of the host species and possibly cause the extinction of a given species, there is nothing to indicate that this has happened in historic times to numerous and cosmopolitan groups of species.

The Stars

There has been a suggestion that mass extinction could have resulted from bursts of high-energy radiation from a nearby supernova. As energy reached the upper limits of the earth's atmosphere, the protective ozone layer was reduced and solar ultraviolet radiation penetrated Earth's atmosphere, reaching the surface. This certainly would be capable of producing mass destruction of most land life but utterly fails to explain how land animals came to be covered by sedimentary rock. And it fails to explain the simultaneous mass extinction that occurred to aquatic organisms within the protection of the sea.

Trace Elements

Another thought has been that excessive amounts or deficiencies of certain metallic trace elements caused past extinctions. While this is an interesting hypothesis, there is no evidence to support it. It is also inconceivable that such variations would have occurred on a world-wide scale.

Climatic Changes

One of the most popular of all hypotheses is that mass extinctions were a result of climatic changes that possibly coincided with the proposed Ice Ages. Large-scale climatic changes would have had adverse effects on biological entities. However, the plant fossil record does not support this hypothesis.

Geologic Upheavals

Baron George Cuvier, the French naturalist of the late 18th and early 19th centuries, suggested that mass extinction occurred as a result of geologic upheavals that produced the mountains of today. This theory was quite popular a century ago but has been generally disregarded by most leading scientists today. It is doubtful that mountain-building of the past would have played a dominant role in the mass extinction of marine and lowland organisms, which make up most of the fossil record. Besides, the mass extinction of most animals does not fit into the proposed time period for the origin of the great mountain systems.

Changing Sea Levels

It is finally proposed that mass extinctions resulted from fluctuations of the sea level. The continual sinking of the sea floor under atolls and flat-topped submarine mountains (guyots) would have been sufficient to produce periodic flooding of the continents as the level of the sea changed. Such flooding could have caused the extinction of many species that were unable to adapt to the new aquatic environment. A shallow sea would cover the continents until another change in the sea level occurred, at which time the shallow sea would drain back into the ocean basin. The receding sea would have left an abundance of marine fossils in addition to the fossils of the animals and plants produced by its original encroachment upon the dry continent.

At first this theory looked very promising, but a more careful study of the fossil record does not indicate that this is a likely explanation for the mass extinctions. Fossils are found buried in sedimentary rock layers that are hundreds and thousands of feet thick. The average depth of the present oceanic sediments is only 2,100 feet. It is believed by most evolutionists that our present oceans have been in existence for some several billion years. If this is all the oceanic sediment that has accumulated in this incredibly long period of time, how could the gradual shift in sea level be capable of producing greater sedimentary deposits than those presently found on the ocean floor?

Certainly the oscillation of the sea level would be capable of explaining mass extinction of many local animal types, but it does not explain how they came to be buried so deeply. In order for this hypothesis to explain the world-wide extinction, it must also explain how the flooding occurred on a global basis.

The Genesis Flood

Though not a popular hypothesis for the evolutionist, the Genesis Flood is a perfectly legitimate explanation of the mass extinction observed in the fossil record. Such flooding would have covered the entire surface of the earth. It was produced by torrential rains that lasted some 40 days. In addition, great subterraneal water sources were involved in the development of the flood. The results would have been catastrophic, and complete extinction would have occurred if some had not been divinely protected.

The Genesis flood would also have been capable of producing the thick sedimentary rock layers that cover nearly every continent on the earth. Animal life would have been swept about by the flood and deposited in gigantic piles that would have been quickly covered with tons of sediment and preserved in fossil forms. Such a flood is certainly consistent with the fossil record and would account for the formation of the huge sedimentary rocks observed today.

Until nearly a century ago, the Genesis Flood was accepted throughout the entire scientific community. Today it has been replaced by the evolutionary theory and the doctrine of uniformitarianism. The Flood Theory is not rejected because of lack of evidence, but because its acceptance would render worthless the inorganic spontaneous generation of life, the entire evolutionary progression of life, and the Geologic Time Table. The Genesis Flood is totally incompatible with the theory of evolution: the two cannot co-exist.

10. A YOUNG OCEAN

Many evolutionists have made a big issue of the similarity between the 3 percent salinity of the oceans and the 3 percent salinity of body fluids. Although just why the blood plasma and other body fluids are 3 percent salt solution is not fully understood, it seems that this degree of salinity is necessary in order for the body to maintain an osmotic balance between the fluid within the body cells and the fluids outside the cells. However, the apparent high correlation between salinity of blood and sea water is not necessarily an indication that one was derived from the other.

To suggest that the correlation between the degrees of salinity of sea water and blood plasma is proof that man's origin began in the sea is also to suggest that the degree of salinity of the oceans has remained essentially the same for a billion years.

The evolutionary theory suggests that the oceans were formed eons ago when the hot surface of the earth finally cooled to below 212°F., allowing rain to fill the ocean basins. Rain is fresh water, so, according to the evolutionary theory, the early ocean was more fresh water than salt water. To suggest that we arose from this ocean of fresh water would in no way explain the 3 percent salinity of the blood plasma. The evolutionary theory seems to contradict itself on this point.

The mineral content dissolved in ocean water, including the degree of salinity, is a result of the erosion of the land. The sediment-rich water that runs from the continents into the oceans carries great deposits of mineral wealth, a process that has continued since the oceans were formed. Thus the oceans have become as salty as they are today. But if the oceans were only 3 percent salty a billion or more years ago, and the same erosional processes are still at work today, shouldn't there have been an increase in the degree of salinity of the oceans? A lot of sediments would have been dumped into the oceans in a billion years.

If the oceans were less salty a billion years ago, there would be no correlation between the salinity of the original oceans and the present degree of salinity of blood plasma.

Dr. Simpson believes that the earth developed its oceans as far back as three billion years ago.

> It is established that approximately 3 billion years ago the earth had a solid, cool crust and that processes of rock oxidation, weathering, and erosion were already going on. This means that there was already water on the surface and that the atmosphere cannot have been extremely different from what it is now.[1]

It is very unlikely that the oceans would have maintained the same degree of salinity in a billion or three billion years if the same processes that originally caused the degree of salinity were in operation during the entire period.

An additional problem is created if erosional processes existed for a billion years. The present erosional rates are simply too great to allow the continents to last anywhere near a billion years. For example, the Colorado River, which is believed to have formed the Grand Canyon, carries an unbelievably large amount of dissolved sediments. Measurements have shown that the average amount of sediment carried by the Colorado at the Grand Canyon site is about 500,000 tons per day! This is equivalent to 100,000 five-ton trucks, emptying a full five ton load every four seconds for 24 hours.

But the Colorado is only one of the major river systems that feed into an ocean. Estimates are that the world system of rivers, melting ice and wind-action deposit as much as 27.5 billion tons of sediment into the oceans every year. Water erosion from the Ice Ages would have caused the present rate of sedimentary deposition to be much greater. However, for the sake of argument, let's assume that the present rate has been fairly constant throughout the past billion years.

On the ocean floor lies a sedimentary layer about 2,100 to 2,900 feet thick which was formed by land erosion. Calculating the area of oceans covering the surface of the earth, this turns out to be an incredible 820 million billion tons of sedimentary deposits on the ocean floor. If we then divide the 820 million billion tons by the present rate of sediments being carried into the oceans, we can derive an approximation of the time it took the present oceanic sediment to build up.

$$\frac{820 \text{ million billion tons}}{27.5 \text{ billion tons/year}} = 30 \text{ million years}$$

In other words, oceanic sediments would have been formed in only 30 million years. This is a very conservative figure; geologists tell us that past erosional processes were probably much greater than at present. This means that the ocean sediments would have been formed in much less than 30 million years.

Of course, if the Genesis Flood occurred, and I believe it did, then sedimentary deposition rates are completely meaningless in determining the time required for the formation of the oceanic sediments. The sediments would have been formed at the time of the Flood.

Estimates show that the average land mass elevation above sea level is less than half the land mass on the ocean floors. The total land mass above sea level is about 383 million billion tons. Just how long will the present continents last at the present erosion rates?

$$\frac{383 \text{ million billion tons}}{27.5 \text{ billion tons/year}} = 14 \text{ million years}$$

Present erosional processes will level the world's continents in about 14 million years. Granted, this is a long time, but it is insignificant when compared to the suggested 4.5 billion-year history of the earth according to the evolutionary theory.

A third serious problem that now faces the evolutionist is the presence of fossils. We are told that many of the fossils lived some 600 million years ago. Erosional processes show us that the continents could not have survived anywhere near that length of time. Geologists have suggested that the continents are being constantly pushed up every 10 to 15 million years and therefore continue to exist. If this is true, how can a 600 million year old fossil still exist? Indeed, how can there be fossil remains older than the continents themselves? Erosion would have destroyed all evidence of fossils or rock layers older than a few million years.

> An early Cambrian shell can end up in the laboratory only if it remained buried for some 600 million years and never was washed out again by erosion in all the intervening upheavals and remodelings of the earth's crust.[2]

Upheavals and remodeling by earth movements would reveal all fossils eventually. There is no way imaginable that a fossil could remain buried for 600 million years, 100 million years or even 50 million years.

11. THE GENESIS FLOOD

Until just over 100 years ago, most people accepted the Genesis Flood as a fact of history. Then arose the doctrine of uniformitarianism which maintained that the present is the key to the past. James Hutton thought that present processes could adequately account for major geological formations in the past. This belief calls for an immensity of time and owes its origin to the theory of evolution. Although not as widely accepted today, its teachings were almost universal at one time. There are many who still hold tenaciously to its concepts.

> There is an important principle for paleontology, geology, or any science that has historical aspects: the present is a key to the past. That principle . . . *the doctrine of uniformitarianism* . . . is now accepted as true by virtually all scientists, and without it there would be no really scientific study of any kind of history.[1]

The doctrine of uniformitarianism has come under attack in recent years because present processes are not adequate to explain many existing geological formations. Rates of erosion today are believed to be less than those in the past, yet present rates would level the earth's continents in only 14 million years.

The earth's magnetic force field has been measured carefully for the last 135 years and is known to be decaying with a most probable half-life of 1,400 years. If the present rate is a key to the past, and should the theory of evolution be correct about the age of the earth, the original magnetic force field would have been as strong as that of a magnetic star!

Dr. James W. Valentine, in an article entitled "The Present is the Key to the Present," questions that the doctrine of uniformitarianism can explain past historical processes. He claims that this doctrine has been vigorously disputed in recent years; that many writers, al-

Decay of Earth's Magnetic Force Field

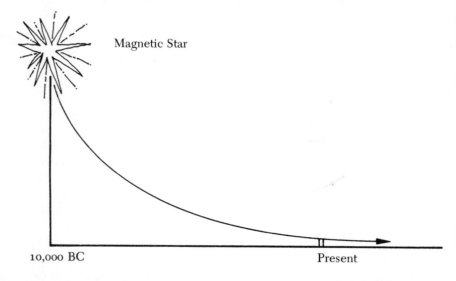

Magnetic Star

10,000 BC   Present

The earth's magnetic force field has been studied for the past 135 years, nearly a century longer than any radiologic clock, and found to have a half-life of about 1400 years. Extrapolating backwards will show that the earth's magnetic force field was as strong as a magnetic star just 12,000 years ago.
Studies have also suggested that there seems to have been a change in the C^{14} concentration in the atmosphere that occurred about 2500 years ago, indicating that concentration has increased at least during the past 10,000 years. This could be due to a decrease in the earth's magnetic force field which has the ability to deflect away much of primary cosmic ray particles that would otherwise reach the earth.

though approaching the subject from different directions, "have agreed that this doctrine is composed partly of meaningless and erroneous components, and some have suggested that it be discarded as a formal assumption of geological science."[2]
   Dr. Edgar Heylmun also questions the reliability of the doctrine of uniformitarianism. He believes that there are too many geological formations that cannot be accounted for by any known present geologic processes and therefore has concluded that "we should not blindly accept the doctrine of uniformitarianism without at least qualifying the concept . . . ."[3]
   Many paleontologists have suggested that the climate of the earth

in the distant past has been milder and more homogeneous than it is today. The present certainly is not a very good key to the past if this is true.

Catastrophism

In opposition to the doctrine of uniformitarianism is the doctrine of catastrophism which maintains that many of the existing geological formations were the result of some cataclysmic event such as a world-wide flood.

The destructive nature of a world flood certainly could account for practically every major geologic formation found on the earth today. It could also account for the reason why so many fossils are found in huge fossil graveyards. But the problem with getting people to accept the doctrine of catastrophism is that the cataclysmic event was a one-time event and is not presently subject to observation or experimentation.

Until the 1800s almost every university in the land taught the Genesis Flood as an historical fact. But with the work of Lyell, Hutton and others, it soon was replaced with the more "scientifically" accepted doctrine of uniformitarianism. The theory of evolution entered into a partnership with the doctrine of uniformitarianism. The two needed each other. Evolution required an immensity of time, and it was believed that uniformitarianism was able to give that time.

Evolutionists are reluctant to admit that the available evidence tends to support the Genesis Flood. If the Genesis Flood is a fact, then the Geologic Time Table, the bible of the evolutionist, is no longer valid. The rich fossil beds could not have been formed by any process operating today. The sedimentary rocks that cover most of the continents of the world could not have been formed by the small amount of flooding that has occurred during present times.

Scoffers in the Last Days

We learn from the Scriptures that the Genesis Flood was a once-for-all, never-to-be-repeated historical event (see Genesis 8:21–9:17; Matthew 24:37–42; and II Peter 3:5–7). Christ acknowledged the fact of the Genesis Flood as did the apostles in many places in the New Testament. In II Peter 3:5–7 we are admonished by the Apostle Peter to be aware of the "last days" for there would be scoffers of the teachings of the Bible. Peter points out that people would deny the Genesis Flood by claiming that things have always been the way they presently are. I believe that this began with the doctrine of uniformitarianism about 1800. Peter points that the doubters will be "willingly ignorant of" the Flood—that is, they will choose not to believe there was a flood.

Peter also indicates that the present world is not like "the world that then was, being overflowed with water." Evidence has suggested that there was a different climate during past times when now extinct animals roamed the earth. Mastodons lived at the North Pole in what appears to have been a tropical environment. Huge coal and oil beds have also been found near the polar regions of the earth. Certainly this indicates a much different climate in the past.

Although the Bible is certainly not a book on science, it has proved to be scientifically accurate. We can gain a great deal of knowledge by the careful study of its pages.

In Genesis we read that God saw the wickedness of man and that it repented Him that He made man. Because God was unable to look upon sin, He determined to destroy the earth with a flood. But Noah found favor in the eyes of God. For the sake of this one righteous man, God would not utterly destroy all life, but allow a remnant to be preserved—Noah and his family as well as specimens of each animal type.

Noah was instructed to build an ark that would provide shelter and safety during the flood to come. The ark was to be 300 cubits in length, 50 cubits in width, and 30 cubits in height. It was to have three decks but only one door at the top deck. Window space was to be provided. The ark's ratio of 300:50, or 6:1, would give the ark stability from pitching and rolling during the Flood. This ratio is not unlike many of the great ships of recent times. The *Great Britian*, designed in 1844, measured almost exactly the same as the ark. It was 322 feet by 51 feet by 32.5 feet. These dimensions, though on a smaller scale, are almost the exact ratio in which the ark was built. The giant tankers of today have a ratio of 7:1, the *Queen Elizabeth* is 8.6:1, and the *Canberra* is 8.2:1.

Was the Ark Big Enough?

Many who object to the Genesis Flood theory claim that the ark was not large enough to serve the purpose for which it was constructed—to hold not only Noah and his family, but also representatives of the entire animal kingdom. There is an estimated 500,000 to a million species of animals. The objection is that the ark would not have been large enough to hold two of each animal species and, in some cases, seven of each species. Since the animals were to be kept alive for a year, provisions for them must also be included on the ark.

Noah's ark was divided into three decks. It is commonly agreed that a cubit is eighteen inches. Therefore, the length of the ark would have been 450 feet, the width some 75 feet, and the height 45 feet. This would figure out to be 500,000 cubic feet per deck, or a total capacity of 1,500,000 cubit feet. Ezekiel records a measurement called a "great cubit" that is believed to have been almost two feet in length. If Noah used this larger unit of measurement, then the ark would have had almost 3,500,000 cubic feet of space. The rectangular construction over present ship designs would have increased the capacity of the ark by 33 percent. Because the ark was not designed for speed, it most likely had a rectangular design.

The space would prove adequate to serve the purpose for which the ark was built. When you realize that there are only 300 species of mammals that are larger than a sheep, and only about a thousand that are larger than a rat, you begin to understand that 1.5 million cubic feet represents a lot of room.

> A barge of such gigantic size, with its thousands of built-in compartments (Genesis 6:14) would have been sufficiently large to carry two of every species of air breathing animal in the world today (and doubtless the tendency toward taxonomic splitting has produced more "species" than can be justified in terms of Genesis "kinds") on only half of its available deck space.[4]

A species may be nothing more than a man-made delineation for a group of homogeneous types. Even Darwin was aware that if all the pigeons were allowed to interbreed, they would all go back to the common rock pigeon—a single species. Noah did not have to make room for every type of dog or cat, but only a representative of a dog-type and a cat-type. Many scientists are coming to realize that a species may only be a generic variation.

Hibernation

Those who reject the Genesis Flood because they cannot imagine how Noah's family could have cared for all the animals aboard the ark, let alone collect them from around the world, should remember that the Flood was the result of a Divine act. We do not read that Noah and his family had to gather the animals of the world and bring them to the ark, but rather that "they came" by Divine instinct. Also, geology has revealed that it would not have been necessary to travel the world over to obtain the animals. The uniformity of climate in the days of Noah would have allowed the animals to live almost anywhere on the globe, and they probably existed in the vicinity of Noah.

The Bible simply is not clear on how Noah was able to care for the animals. For the solution of this problem we can only guess. Dr. John E. Whitcomb explains that the hibernating ability of many animals may have been imposed on all the animals of the ark for the duration of the Flood: "We believe that (God) supernaturally imposed a year-long hibernation or estivation experience, whereby the bodily functions of these animals were reduced to a minimum, and thus removed the burden of their care completely from the hands of Noah and his family."[5]

The Source of the Flood Water

It is obvious that there is not enough water on the earth today to cover the mountains of the present globe. I believe that the condition of the earth before the Flood was very different from what it is today. The Apostle Peter refers to the time before the Flood as "the world that was."

From Genesis we learn that the original creation had a water vapor layer above the earth which would not only have protected the earth from harmful solar radiations, but also may have been the reason for the longevity of so many Bible patriarchs. Exposure to solar radiation such as ultraviolet or X-rays appears to shorten life. (It is common knowledge that radiologists live an average of seven years less than their counterparts in other medical fields.)

This layer would also have had a warming effect and would have provided a uniform temperature over the entire globe. It could also be the source of much of the water of the Genesis Flood. We are told that it did not rain until the time of the Flood, but that a mist went up from the ground and provided moisture for the earth's plant life.

So great was the amount of water in the transparent vapor layer above the earth that when the Flood rains began, it required a full 40 days and nights of continuous rainfall to empty the water in the layer. This certainly was not a gentle rain, but fell as a torrential downpour without any letup. When the rains began to fall, Noah and his family, with the animals to be spared, were safely aboard the ark. The flood continued for several weeks, and the flood waters were maintained for another 110 days.

Not only did the Flood contain water from the vapor layer above the earth, but we also read in Genesis 7:11 that "all the fountains of the deep" were released "on the same day." The ground water involvement implies that great geologic activity was present during the Flood. The earth was being completely reshaped; mountains were being formed and volcanoes were erupting at maximum. The entire earth was being shaken.

The flood water rose to fifteen cubits (22.5 feet) above the highest mountain at that time and remained at that level for several months. But eventually the waters began to recede and drain into the newly formed ocean basins. As the ocean basins sank to their present levels, mountains rose to their new heights. Dr. Whitcomb comments on this very likely condition:

> Since the breaking up of the fountains of the great deep involved the uplift of ocean floors, the stopping of these "fountains" must refer to a reversal of this action, whereby new and much deeper ocean basins were formed to serve as vast reservoirs for the two oceans which were separated from each other by the atmospheric expanse before the Flood (Genesis 1:7).[6]

Does the Genesis account actually indicate that every mountain of the entire earth was covered with water? I believe it does. In Psalms 104:6 we read that "the waters stood above the mountains." Further indications are given that Whitcomb's postulate of the great earth diastropisms actually occurred; in Psalms 104:8 in the New American Standard Bible we read: "The mountains rose, the valleys sank down to the place which Thou didst establish for them."

Even the great abundance of water coming down from the water vapor above the earth and the breaking up of waters from the depth of the earth would not have provided enough water to cover the earth's present mountain systems. But the breaking up of the deep implies that the ocean floor rose. If it is assumed that the mountains were not the 20,000 feet we observe today, it becomes possible that the Genesis Flood could easily have covered the entire globe. Again, Dr. Whitcomb comments:

> It is frequently maintained, and rightfully so, that there simply is not enough water in our present oceans to cover all the mountains of the earth, even if ocean basins could somehow be pushed up to present sea levels, for there are many mountains more than 20,000 feet high, with an average of only 12,000 feet of water to cover them. But if these mountains (with their marine fossils) rose to their present heights *since* the Flood, we may assume that none of the "high mountains" that existed before the Flood (Genesis 7:19) were more than 6,000 to 7,000 feet high.[7]

What we read in Psalms 104:8 most likely refers to the time when the mountains rose to their present heights. This would also explain why marine fossils are often found high on mountain tops well above the 12,000-foot level.

Should the earth's surface ever come to be made level, this would certainly become a water planet. The 330 million cubic miles of water in the earth's oceans would be capable of covering the surface to a depth of some 12,000 feet.

Not a Local Flood

Some have suggested that a local flood occurred in the days of Noah rather than a world-wide flood. But this is not consistent with what is recorded in Genesis 7:19–20: " . . . and *all* the high mountains that were under the whole heaven were covered." Whitcomb has pointed out that even if just one high mountain were covered for this period of time, such a depth would have existed world-wide. But the major objection to the theory of a local flood is in the purpose of the ark. Why take 120 years to construct such a monstrous barge if the flood were only to be local? Noah could have left the area as did Lot and his family when Lot was warned that the city of Sodom was to be destroyed. The purpose of the ark was rather meaningless if this were the case. Given 120 years, Noah could have led his family, at a rate of just one hundred miles per year, over 12,000 miles from the area to be destroyed. Certainly this would have been a much more logical approach to the problem than constructing an ark.

Is This Noah's Ark?

We read that the ark came to rest on the mountain of Ararat. Today there exists a wooden structure on Mt. Ararat that has puzzled scientists throughout the world. The structure has been measured by radio soundings through the glacier in which it rests. Its dimensions are almost exactly the same as those of the ark. What is a structure such as this doing 15,000 feet up the side of a rocky mountain? How did it get there? Could this be the ark built by Noah?

Those who have scaled the difficult mountain of Ararat and have seen this structure say it matches the description of the ark as given in Genesis. Should this structure actually prove to be Noah's ark, the Geologic Time Table certainly must be changed.

Magnitude of the Flood

The magnitude of the Genesis Flood would certainly have left its mark on the face of the earth. There is simply no way that a worldwide flood could have occurred without leaving evidence of its destructive power. Admittedly, however, such a flood could only have been the result of a supernatural act by a Divine Being.

The destruction caused by moving water is known by many—you don't need a science degree to know that moving water is a powerful force. Primitive mining operations once used water as a method to literally move mountains. The method was called the "Placer-method of mining" and employed a powerful jet of water directed at a hillside. So powerful was this jet stream of water that it could kill a man standing 300 feet from the nozzle. Obviously, and for good reason, it was soon outlawed and is no longer practiced. Many hillsides, however, still show the ugly scars left by this very destructive mining method.

Flood waters have been known to move boulders weighing tons for great distances. At Cherbourg, France, storm waves hurled 7,000-pound stones over a 20-foot high breakwater. These same waves moved 65-ton concrete blocks a distance of some 60 feet!

Just what would have been the effects produced by the Genesis Flood? For this we may turn to a description given by Dr. Henry Morris (as quoted by Dr. Whitcomb) who has a Ph.D. in hydrology and hydraulics from the University of Minnesota:

> Dr. Morris has pointed out that according to the law of hydro-dynamic selectivity a flood of the magnitude described in Genesis, with its unbelievably vast complex of sediment-saturated currents, would of necessity produce horizontal, superimposed layers of materials, selected by the moving waters according to their specific gravity and sphericity. As each current of water slowed down and deposited its load, another current would come from perhaps a different direction, carrying somewhat different types of materials, depositing them on top of the first layer without disturbing it. Thus, as various currents moved across the earth during the months of the Flood, a great series of sedimentary strata would be formed in various parts of the earth, in some cases to depths of many thousands of feet.[8]

Anyone who visits the Grand Canyon in Arizona will at once notice the uniformity in which the various layers have been deposited. There is little evidence of tilting or uplifting. When you learn that this area is only a small part of the huge sedimentary layers making up the southwest United States, you begin to realize the magnitude of the sedimentary rock deposit of the past. Only a flood of immense size could have produced such even sedimentary deposits. We know of no process in operation today that is capable of forming such huge sedimentary layers.

In addition to the evidence given by the present sedimentary layers as having been the result of a world flood, the abundance of fossils today could not have formed to the degree we find them if they had been preserved by processes operating today.

> Not only do sedimentary deposits demand the dynamics of a gigantic flood for adequate explanation, but so also do the fossils of billions of plants and animals that are found within them. This indeed is a serious problem for evolutionary uniformitarianism, for largescale fossilization is simply *not* occurring anywhere in the world today.[9]

Flood Traditions

Many people have chosen not to believe the Genesis account of the Flood and thus reject a very reasonable explanation for existing geological formation that otherwise cannot be accounted for. But the Genesis Flood simply cannot be discarded that easily. If such an event occurred, you would expect to find records of it in the traditions of people throughout the world. The survivors of such a catastrophe would pass on to their children the events that occurred during that time. And so as the tradition is passed from one generation to another, we expect to find flood traditions throughout the world. And this is exactly what we find.

It is to be expected that the traditions vary, but there are certain similar characteristics common in most of them:

1. There was destruction by water of the entire human race and all other living things.

2. An ark, or type of boat, is the means that allowed only a few to escape the destruction of the flood.

3. And each tradition has a remnant preserved to perpetuate the human race.

Dr. Johannes Riem has made an extensive study of flood traditions and has reported his findings in *Die Sintfut in Sage und Wissenschaft*. A significant statement is made in the introduction to his work:

> Among all traditions there is none so general, so widespread on earth, and so apt to show what may develop from the same material according to the varying spiritual character of a people as the Flood tradition. Lengthy and thorough discussions with Dr. Kunike have convinced me of the evident correctness of his position that the fact of the Deluge is granted because at the basis of all myth, particularly nature myths, there is a real fact, but that during a subsequent period the material was given its present mythical character and form.[10]

Flood traditions are most common in Asia and on the islands immediately south of Asia and on the North American continent. Some flood traditions have been found in Africa but not nearly as abundantly as on other continents. Historical studies on Babylonian, Assyrian and Sumerian Flood traditions are numerous. Dr. Richard Andree has collected over 88 different flood traditions. Of these, 20 are in Asia, five in Europe, seven in Africa, ten in Australia and the South Sea Islands, and 46 are among American aborigines.

Hugh Miller, the Scottish geologist of the last century, was amazed at the impact that the flood tradition has had on so many people of so many different countries:

> There is, however, one special tradition which seems to be more deeply impressed and more widely spread than any of the others. The destruction of well-nigh the whole human race,

in an early age of the world's history, by a great deluge, appears to have so impressed the minds of the few survivors, and seems to have been handed down to their children, in consequence, with such terror-struck impressiveness that their remote descendents of the present day have not even yet forgotten it. It appears in almost every mythology, and lives in the most distant countries, and among the most barbarous tribes.[11]

The American Indian tribe of Athapascan found on the West Coast have a flood tradition that at one time in the past the rain began to fall until "the waters of the oceans came together" and all living things were drowned. The Great Spirit then remade all living things on the earth.

The Papago Indians of Arizona have a flood tradition in which a great flood destroyed all flesh except Montezuma and a coyote who was his friend. Montezuma and the coyote escaped the destruction of the flood by hollowing out a boat from a log. The coyote sealed the boat, making certain that his friend would be safe. Other American Indian legends are similar to this one but have substituted either an eagle or wolf for the coyote.

The Arapaho believe that the world was covered by a flood except for a single tall mountain. A lone Indian named Arapaho was left stranded on the top. Three ducks came to Arapaho, and he commanded them to dive deep into the water and bring up some mud. This they did. At the moment they brought the mud up, the waters of the earth were parted. Arapaho became the sole possessor of the earth and began to create anew all life.

In the Northwest, the Algonquins have a tradition that in the past men became very evil. At that time a powerful snake that was the enemy of all living things came and caused a flood that destroyed all men and living creatures. Only a few were saved by Manabozho, the grandfather of the human race and all living things. Manabozho saved the remnant by making a boat so that they could escape. When the land dried, Manabozho restored everything as it was before the flood. The snake, called "the evil one," then went away.

The Spanish historian, Herrera, tells of flood traditions in Brazil and Peru. The ancient Indians of Peru had a tradition in which all the peoples of the world were drowned save six who were saved in a large boat. The Mechoachens have a legend that a single family saved itself and many animals from a flood that covered the world by building a huge boat.

The ancient and original inhabitants of Cuba have perhaps the most remarkable flood tradition:

> . . . an old man, knowing the deluge was to come, built a great ship and went into it with his family and an abundance of animals; and that, wearying during the continuance of the flood, he sent out a crow, which at first did not return, staying to feed on dead bodies, but afterwards returned bearing with it a green branch.[12]

Many have discredited this last account because it too closely resembles the Genesis account of the Biblical Flood. They believe the tradition resulted from stories left by some Christian missionary who happened to wander through Cuba at some time in the past. But when this legend is studied in the light of the many other ancient flood traditions, it is entirely probable that the story was handed down for generations without the intervention of a missionary.

There are flood traditions in Mexico. Coxcox, also called Tezpi by some tribes, was able to save himself, his wife, his children, some animals, and some grain from a great flood by using a large boat. Legend has it that Coxcox then sent out birds to look for dry land. Only the hummingbird returned with a branch covered with leaves.

The ancient Maya culture also records a flood tradition. Natives of Sudan call Lake Chad in Bornu Bahar *el Nuh* (the Lake of Noah) and believe a flood that submerged the whole earth had its origin in this lake. The Hottentots call the progenitor of their race *Noh* and *Hingnoh*.

Other flood traditions may be found in ancient cultures of Hawaii, Sumatra, Alaska, India, China, Egypt, Greece and Italy.

The Significance of Flood Traditions

The significance of flood traditions is that they all bear some resemblance to the Genesis Flood. Some may have come from zealous missionaries, but not all. We now are faced with a very important question: If no flood of world-wide magnitude took place, why do so many ancient cultures have such similar flood traditions? I believe that the traditions that have been handed down from one generation to another only serve as further proof that at one time in the past the entire world was covered by a flood—the Genesis Flood.

12. SEARCH FOR THE ANTIQUITY OF MAN

The search for the antiquity of man is based on the assumption that the evolution of man is a fact. Although the search has been conducted by very sincere men and women, it has been based on the assumption that man evolved from less complex forms. Since all the searchers have been trained in the doctrine of evolution, any find is interpreted along the evolutionary line of thinking. Therefore, the only evidence considered is that which looks like it might fit into the evolutionary ascent of man.

When Dubois found his Java Man on the banks of the Solo River, it was not the result of an accidental discovery, but rather the result of a "preconceived" search in which the Java Man had already been named. Furthermore, all evidence that proved contradictory to Java Man was overlooked, cast aside or hidden.

We have known since 1933 that there are human and dinosaur footprints in the same rock layer in Texas. In Utah fossilized sandals were found showing that trilobites and man existed at the same time. Yet in the search for the antiquity of man, these two findings are not mentioned in the texts. They don't fit into the plan of things, so the evolutionists have left them out. It is unfortunate that this is the case, for biasness is unfair to the student who is searching for the truth. He is not being told the complete story but rather only the part that supports the doctrine of evolution. Consider just part of what has been produced by the evolutionists as proof of man's antiquity:

Ramapithecus

Evolutionists generally agree that a common ancestor of both man and ape existed about 15 million years ago. This common ancestor produced two lines, one of which supposedly led to the apes and the other to man. The line that led to man is known as *Ramapithecus*.

The fossil evidence of *Ramapithecus* is composed solely of an upper jaw fragment and a few teeth—very similar to the fossil evidence of Nebraskan Man which proved to be a pig. It is believed that the front teeth were relatively small in comparison to the cheek teeth as is the case in the dental structure of man. It is furthermore assumed that the jaw of *Ramapithecus* is parabolic rather than U-shaped (see diagram).

However, dental measurements made by Dr. Eckhardt on *Ramapithecus* and *Dryopithecus*, a true fossil ape, show less variation than a similar comparison of living chimpanzees at a research center and a wild population of chimpanzees in Liberia. In other words, there is greater variation among a living group of apes than there is between *Dryopithecus*, a fossil ape, and *Ramapithecus* which evolutionists believe gave rise to man.[1]

Dr. Gish has reported that similar comparisons to five other species of *Dryopithecus* and to *Kenyapithecus*, believed to be the oldest hominid form yet discovered in East Africa, produced very little variation. Measurements show that these three creatures, *Ramapithecus*, *Dryopithecus*, and *Kenyapithecus*, more likely than not belonged to the same species. Since dental measurements show little variation among these proposed hominid ancestors of man, why assume that they were all different species? Evolutionists continue to report their findings as different species of man-like creatures, all of which somehow have managed to fit into the evolutionary scheme of things. Consider the following report on *Ramapithecus*:

> Anthropologists theorize that once out of the forest, *Ramapithecus* began to evolve rapidly. The process of natural selection favored those of his genus who could stand up; an erect position enabled them to see over the tall grass to spot and hunt their prey—and to see and escape the carnivores that preyed on them. Thus they were able to survive longer and produce more offspring, who shared their physical characteristics. After many generations of selection, the savanna-dwellers had evolved into upright-standing animals distinctly different from the forest-dwelling relatives they had left behind.[2]

Does the fossil record suggest that this is what really happened, or is this mere conjecture based on the philosophy of evolution? The same article continues:

> Though scientists have found practically no telltale fossils from

Comparison between *Australopithecus* and chimpanzee dentition

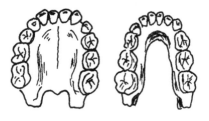

Australopithecus

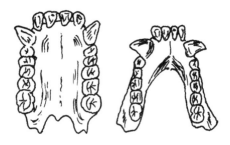

Chimpanzee

Although considerable difference exists between the parabolic-shaped dentition of *Australopithecus* and the U-shaped dentition of the chimpanzee, this is not proof that *Australopithecus* was man-like. Skull 1470, found by Richard Leakey, goes back further than *Australopithecus*. Fossil evidence has suggested that modern man goes back as far as *Australopithecus*.

the crucial period between 8 million and 5 million years ago, anthropologists speculate that some time toward the end of this period the hominid line split into the species *Australopithecus robustus* and *africanus*.[3]

The whole evolutionary interpretation of *Ramapithecus'* lifestyle is sheer speculation and not founded on real evidence. "There are no telltale fossils from this crucial period ... " for the scientist to study. Furthermore, the fragmentary fossil remains of *Ramapithecus* too closely resemble the fossil ape, *Dryopithecus*, to be considered anything other than a true ape.

In addition, there is a living baboon, *Theropithecus galada*, in the highlands of Ethiopia that has incisors and canines which are also small in comparison to the cheek teeth. This baboon also has a short face and other man-like facial characteristics that are believed to have been possessed by both *Ramapithecus* and *Australopithecus*. It is very possible that *Ramapithecus* is nothing more than a variety of the living baboon *Theropithecus*. Dr. Elwyn Simons, Duke University Center for the Study of Primate Biology and History, has made the following statement on the significance of *Ramapithecus* in relation to the evolutionary doctrine: "Ramapithecus is ideally structured to be an ancestor of hominids. If he isn't, we don't have anything else that is."[4]

Australopithecus

In 1924 Raymond Dart discovered in a limestone quarry at Taung a skull that he believed was a hominid ancestor. After careful examination of the flat-like teeth, Dart made the announcement that his new find, *Australopithecus africanus* (the "southern ape") was truly hominid. The cranial capacity of this creature was about 500 cc, or less than a third of that of man, whose cranial capacity measures about 1400 cc.

In 1939 a larger *Australopithecus robustus* was found that had more massive teeth and jaws and possessed sagittal and supramastoid crests (bony ridges) commonly associated with gorillas. Most scientists now believe that *Australopithecus robustus* and *africanus* to be the male and female respectively of a single species of apes.

Zinjanthropus bosei, or the "East African man," found by Louis and Mary Leakey at Olduvai Gorge in Tanzania, has turned out to be just a variety of *Australopithecus*.

Jonathan Leakey, the older son of Louis Leakey, unearthed a fossil skull in 1961 that had a brain capacity of nearly 700 cc. Jonathan's father named the skull *Homo habilis*, or "handy man," because it was believed that this creature was capable of tool-making. But evidence now shows that *Homo habilis* coexisted with *Australopithecus*. This means that *H. habilis* could not have descended from the former. Some now even believe that *H. habilis* may be just another variety of *Australopithecus*.

A nearly complete skeleton of *Australopithecus* was found in 1974 in a sediment layer believed to be almost 3 million years old. Many believe that the shape of the pelvis suggests that this find, named "Lucy," gives evidence that *Australopithecus* may have walked upright. But again, not all are willing to accept this idea. Richard Leakey, son of Louis Leakey, has published evidence indicating that "the *Australopithecines* were long-armed, short-legged, knuckle-walkers, similar to extant African apes."[5]

In addition, a skull comparison between *Australopithecus* and a modern orang produced little differences; only minor variations exist between the two. *Australopithecus* has proved to be an ape and not hominid by any means—except in the mind of the evolutionist.

Java Man

Perhaps the most intriguing and mysterious find ever produced was that of Java Man, *Pithecanthropus erectus*, "erect ape-man," found in 1891 by the Dutch physician, Dubois, near the village of Trinil, Java. Dubois had managed to get himself an assignment to this area in hopes that he would discover the "dream creature" of German naturalist Haeckel, a vivid writer who had an imaginary ancestry for man and had selected the name for this creature to be *Pithecanthropus alalus*, or the "speechless apeman."

While digging on the bank of the Solo River, Dubois found a skull cap which he estimated had a brain capacity of almost 900 cc. A year later, some 50 feet away, a femur was found. Dubois assumed that the skull cap and femur belonged to each other. Two molar teeth were also found in the same vicinity and were assumed to belong to the skull cap. In 1898 a third tooth, a premolar, was found and placed along with the other finds. This scanty collection became known as Java Man.

Dubois, however, concealed the fact that he had also found two human skulls at the same level in the nearby Wadjak village. The skulls had a cranial capacity of about 1550 to 1650 cc. This is somewhat greater than the present human skull average. Dubois was afraid that the two Wadjak skulls would cause serious doubts about the credibility of Java Man and did not reveal until just before his death in 1922 that these two skulls existed. It was also then that he admitted Java Man was probably nothing more than a large gibbon.

It turned out that the two molars belonged to an orang and the premolar to a true man. But nevertheless, Java Man did fit into the evolutionary picture, and there are those who still maintain that this creature was hominid.

Peking Man

Peking Man, *Sinanthropus pekinensis*, resulted from fossil fragments found in the 1920s and 1930s at Choukoutien, about 25 miles from Peking. The finds produced some 30 skulls, 11 mandibles, and about 147 teeth. The story is told that these finds were made in a "lower cave" of a limestone cliff. Fragments of modern man were also found higher up the cliff in an alleged "upper cave." In addition, several species of animals left fossil remains throughout the entire cliff. There is absolutely no evolutionary variations in these many animal species.

Today, everything except two teeth have mysteriously disappeared. The bones of Peking Man were turned over to the U.S. Marines in China in 1941 shortly before the Japanese attack on Pearl Harbor. No one knows what happened to the fossils since that time. Despite a longstanding offer of $150,000 reward that was finally withdrawn in October, 1977, they have never been found.

All that exists today of Peking Man are models made by Franz Weidenreich and the descriptions left by a few investigators who were totally committed to the doctrine that supports the evolution of man.

It has been suggested that *S. pekinensis* was found in the same limestone cliff at a much lower level than the fossils of modern man. Yet the fossil remains of about 100 different animal species also found in various levels of the cliff failed to show any evolutionary progression from the bottom of the cliff to the top of the cliff.

In addition, all the skulls were damaged and were missing the lower jaw. The cranial capacity was between 900 and 1200 cc. Most authorities have agreed that all of the *Sinanthropus* individuals had been killed and eaten. The evidence suggests that the skulls had been bashed in near the base and the brains extracted. The question now is, Who were the hunters?

Weidenreich and most other evolutionists believe that *Sinanthropus* were cannibals and actually fed on each other. If it were not for the fact that human skulls had been found in the same limestone cliff, this line of reasoning would almost have been plausible. The presence of man in the same area would naturally nullify any evolutionary hypothesis.

The Reverend Patrick O'Connell, a Roman Catholic priest, was in China at the time of the Choukoutien digs. He studied very carefully the accounts of the findings and noted many discrepancies between the models of Franz Weidenreich and the written accounts of the actual fossils. There is doubt that there ever was an upper cave, according to O'Connell.

Evidence exists that suggests this limestone cliff was the site of a large-scale limestone quarry in past times. Quartz stones with soot layers on just one side suggest that lime kilns had been constructed and operated during this time. Enormous heaps of ashes and tools of fine workmanship that have been found at the site tend to support this theory. Rev. O'Connell also remembers that fossil remains of ten human individuals were found at the same level and site where the *Sinanthropus* skulls were found.

The evidence suggests that the Choukoutien site was a limestone quarry, operated by humans, and the *Sianthropus* skulls were actually large monkeys (macaques) or baboons that had been killed and eaten by the human workers.

No matter how hard he tried, Weidenreich's attempts to make models of *Sinanthropus* could not be free of the biasness of his evolutionary training and philosophy. Weidenreich attempted to reconstruct the skull of *Sinanthropus* from memory and the descriptions left by the original observations. Rev. O'Connell reports that there are many contradictions between Weidenreich's model and the descriptions left at the time of the find.

It was during this same time, 1922, that the Nebraskan Man, *Hesperopithecus haroldcookii*, was discovered in western Nebraska. This find consisted of nothing more than a single tooth which was used as evidence of the validity of evolution in the famous Scopes' Trial. But by 1927 the tooth was discovered not to belong to a pre-man, but rather to an extinct pig.

Piltdown Man

The Piltdown Man was found in a gravel pit near Piltdown, England, in 1912. The fossils consisted of a mandible and part of a skull. It was given the name *Eanthropus dowsoni*, or "dawn man," and judged to be 500,000 years old. But dawn man proved to be a fraud.

By 1950 the fluoride dating method had been developed and clearly showed that the skull had significant amounts of fluoride that could date it to a few thousand years old, but the mandible contained hardly any fluoride. A more careful investigation revealed that the bones had been treated with iron salts and purposely scratched with a file to make them look old.

Recent testimony has been given to suggest that the culprit of the Piltdown hoax may have been William Johnson Sollas, an Oxford anthropology professor. Sollas felt insulted and threatened by a rising scientist, Arthur Smith Woodward, who had dared criticize a presentation made by the professor. *Time Magazine* published an article (November 13, 1978) that suggests Sollas may have attempted to avenge his deflated ego by treating a skull with potassium bichromate to give it an appearance of great antiquity and place it with some ape's teeth he "borrowed" from the anatomy department.

Sollas planted the hoax in hopes that Woodward would fall for the trick at which time Sollas would admit to the hoax, thereby discrediting Woodward as a scientist. But the plan backfired when not only did Woodward stake his reputation on the authenticity of the find, but so did the entire scientific community. Sollas realized he would not be able to admit that Piltdown Man was a hoax of his own making and chose instead to remain silent rather than face being ostracized by his colleagues.

Neanderthal Man

About a century ago in a cave in the Neanderthal Valley near Dusseldorf, Germany, a fossil remain was found and given the name *Homo neanderthalensis*. It was later discovered that the individual had been crippled with arthritis; further evidence suggests that these people suffered a Vitamin D deficiency that produced rickets, a softening of the bones and consequent malformation.

From what we know today, if Neanderthal Man stood fully erect, he would be indistinguishable from modern man. In fact, he more than likely was *Homo sapien*, a true modern man. Cro-magnon and Swanscombe Man have likewise proved to be modern man.

Skull 1470

Perhaps the most upsetting discovery for the evolutionists was made by Richard Leakey at Lake Rudolf in North Kenya. Leakey announced that he had found a fossil skull with a brain capacity of about 800 cc and called it "1470" after its National Museums of Kenya catalogue number. Leakey believed that the skull went back as far as three million years. Although on the small side, the skull is that of modern man. Nothing is known, however, about the age or sex of "1470." Leg bones of "1470" indicate that his individual walked upright like a modern man.

The significance of this find is that it demonstrates that modern man goes back as far as those from which he supposedly descended. In other words, Skull 1470 has dealt a severe blow to all previously held theories as to the ancestry of man. Evolutionists should certainly be quick to delete *Australopithecus* from the proposed evolutionary "tree of life," because Skull 1470 clearly indicates that a large-brained, truly upright and bipedal form of the genus *Homo* co-existed with the *Australopithecines*.

Just what has Richard Leakey's find contributed to the present study of the antiquity of man? It has shattered every theory so far presented, particularly those of his famous father, the late Louis B. Leakey. Dr. Gish is convinced that because of Skull 1470, "Every single book on anthropology, every article on the evolution of man, every drawing of man's family tree will have to be junked. They are apparently wrong."[6]

Dr. Gish points out that if Richard Leakey's find is accepted, then he will have completely upset all his father's theories on the possibility of the *Australopithecines* having played a role in the origin of man. Such a position is supportive of the creationist's position, which insists that man and apes have always been contemporary. Dr. Gish believes that all courses on anthropology must be completely rewritten if Leakey's Skull 1470 proves to be authentic: "If Richard Leakey's evaluation of his latest find, Skull 1470, is accepted, he will have succeeded not only in shattering completely his father's theories . . . but everyone else's as well."[7]

Let's Start Over Again

Dr. Francis Ivanhoe has produced evidence that the teeth and bones of Neanderthal Man show the characteristic rickets ring pattern. Neanderthal was once believed to be definite link between man and ape-like creatures, but such a belief has been almost entirely abandoned in scientific circles. Neanderthal is classified as *Homo sapiens*—just like you and me. Gradually, evidence has been produced that discredits almost every "ape-man" hypotheses.

And now, with the more recent discovery of Skull 1470, Richard Leakey has appealed for more funds to begin the search for the antiquity of man all over again!

World Population Growth Rates

Dr. Henry Morris, Director of the Institute for Creation Research, has demonstrated the seriousness of the problem when it is assumed that man has been on the earth for a million years. This would represent about 25,000 generations that would have lived during this million-year period. Many scientists are now convinced, however, that man goes back several millions of years.

The average family in the world today has 3.6 children. This gives an annual world population growth rate of about 2%. Many environmentalists and concerned people now realize that a 2% population growth rate will very soon produce too many people for the world to feed and are pleading for "zero population growth." This does not mean married couples are to have no children but that the average family would have 2.1 children. Figures indicate that if this were the case, 2.1 children per family average world-wide, then the world population would remain the same, thereby reducing the annual world population growth rate to 0%.

Dr. Morris is concerned with the question of how long it took the world population to reach the 4 billion mark. He has calculated that if the average family during the assumed million-year history of man had just 2.5 children, this would produce an annual population growth rate of only 0.5%—far less than the present observed growth rate. This 0.5% growth rate would have produced a final population at the end of the million-year period (25,000 generations) of over 20^{2100} . To understand just how many people this would be, realize that the entire universe is capable of holding only 10^{130} electrons. An electron, the subatomic particle of the atom that circles the nucleus, is infinitely smaller than a human being.

Just how long would it take the world to reach the present population, assuming that each family averaged only 2.5 children, or a growth rate of only 0.5% annually? According to Dr. Morris' calcula-

World Population Growth Curve

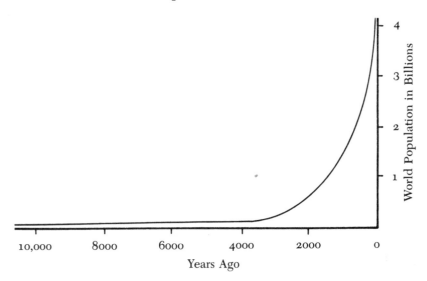

It is suggested that about 110 billion individuals have passed their days, and left their bones, on this crowded planet. If this were true, then the average world population would only be 110,000 persons per year, assuming a million year history. This would suggest that the human population has been practicing "zero population growth" for almost its entire history until only in very recent years.

tions, the present world population would have been reached in only about 4,000 years.

For the evolutionists who insist that man covers a million-year history, then some explanation must be given that can adequately account for the missing billions and billions of persons who would have died during this million-year period. Why are other fossils so abundant and those of man so scarce?

Israel and Growth Rates

The nation of Israel began some 3,700 years ago with the patriarch Jacob and serves as an excellent example of how quickly a nation can populate itself. Few nations have suffered the effects of pestilence

and wars as have the Israelites. They have suffered attempts of gen-
ocide at the hands of the ancient Assyrians, Babylonians, and Romans. Their numbers have often been reduced by the inhumane
behavior of surrounding nations. In 70 A.D. they were finally driven
from their homeland and scattered throughout many nations of the
world. Hitler murdered millions in his attempt to annihilate the descendents of Jacob, but he failed, as did the Assyrians, Babylonians,
and Romans. Israel exists today not only as a people but as a nation.

Given a generation of 43 years and an average family of 2.4 children, representing an annual growth rate of less than 0.5%, this
would still allow for 13,900,000 Israelites to be living today. As of
1970 there were some 14,000,000 Jews living in the United States
alone.

The effects of war have not demonstrated a significantly measurable effect on the population growth rates of this people. This example is given only to benefit those who believe the effects of war
have held the population of the world in check.

The human population of the earth has been increasing since its
beginning. If mankind goes back hundreds of thousands of years,
why did the human population not reach its present population thousands of years ago? As early as 1798, Thomas Malthus began to sound
the alarm concerning problems of overpopulation if the growth rates
were allowed to continue unchecked. He warned that a continuing
increase in the world population would lead to widespread misery
and starvation. Today about two-thirds of the people of the world are
going hungry.

Julian Huxley has concluded that the population of the world has
been increasing since before the dawn of history. He estimates that
before the discovery of agriculture, about 6,000 B.C., the total population was probably less than 20 million. To suggest that it has taken
almost a million years to develop that 20 million people is to suggest
that the human population has been able to practice zero population
growth for almost a million years. That is very unlikely.

13. WHY CREATIONISM ?

Individuals, particularly Christians, who are not aware of the lack of evidence to support evolution will still attempt to put meaning into the concept of life and the origin of the universe. True evolution holds that life is the result of nondirected chemical activities that through random chance happenings managed to create life. According to the evolutionist, life has no purpose, no direction, no meaning. But the Christian is keenly aware that this simply cannot be the case; that life does have purpose, direction and meaning.

Unfortunately, the Christian has been told that if he is to believe in the Biblical account of creation, he must do so against the overwhelming evidence that has proved evolution to be a fact. To believe in creation is to be religious; and to be religious requires a faith that must stand against the evidence at hand. Diagrams, charts and pictures have been placed in textbooks that supposedly attest to the validity of evolution. But these books fail to show their readers that much of the evidence presented is pure conjecture on the part of the authors.

Since 1933 we have known that dinosaurs and man lived at the same time, but our textbooks continue to convey the idea that dinosaurs died as a result of a drying Earth some 70 million years before man came on the scene. We know that the dinosaurs died not in a desert, but in a flood that sometimes piled their bodies in huge stacks.

Since there is no way at present to prove scientifically the way in which the earth, the universe or life came into existence, we must choose the theory that best fits the evidence available to us. Since the evolutionary theory receives 99.9 percent of the backing of the present educational systems (public and private), it is no wonder that young Christians soon disregard, if not completely reject, the Biblical account of creation. Unfortunately, this decision is reached not after a careful consideration of all the available facts, but as a result

The Four Theories on the Origin of the Earth

	SIX DAYS	EVOLUTION	DAY-AGE	GAP
Who?	God	"ex nihilo"	God	God
When?	less than 10,000 years ago	4.5 billion years ago	4.5 billion years ago	4.5 billion years ago
How?	By the Word of God Heb.11:3	Spontaneous generation & organic evolution	Divinely guided & controlled evolution	By the Word of God . . . The World had to be recreated as a result of the fall of Satan
Why?	God's Glory Eph. 1:12	?	God's Glory	God's Glory

of only one side having been presented—the case for evolution. The evidence presented is often biased and made to sound more convincing than it actually is. But if *all* the evidence were to be presented—assuring true academic freedom—I wonder how many would continue to adhere to evolution?

Many Christians have been forced to adjust their thinking to include the evolutionary doctrine within their Christian faith. Knowing that the Bible was written under the divine revelation of God has caused many Christians to attempt to combine the two—creation and evolution. This has led to the formation of such unnecessary theories as the Day-Age and the Gap Theory. With the addition of these two theories, there are now four general theories concerning the study of origins: Six-Day Biblical account of creation, Inorganic/Organic Evolution, Day-Age Theory and the Gap Theory. There are without doubt other theories that could be presented, but their presence would serve no purpose because the argument quickly narrows down to just two: the Six-Day Biblical account and Inorganic/Organic Evolution.

The Day-Age Theory

The Day-Age Theory of origins is based on the idea that "day," as used in Genesis, actually refers to an indefinitely long period of time. Each day could possibly represent millions of years. Many evolutionists have "helped" Christians to accept the theory of evolution by alluding to the belief that a Genesis day could not refer to a 24-hour day and therefore must refer only to a period of time, a very long period of time.

The Hebrew word used in Genesis for day is *yom* and always refers to a single 24-hour day; it is never used as an indefinite period of time. Other references in the Bible seem to support the creative acts of God as having taken place in a literal six-day period. See Exodus 20:11. There is a Hebrew word, *olam*, that conveys the concept of an indefinitely long period of time. Why would Moses, the writer of Genesis, use *yom* if he actually meant *olam*?

The Day-Age Theory runs into further problems that excludes its right for further consideration as an explanation for the origin of the earth and life. Consider just a few of these:

1. The Genesis account (Genesis 1:11) states that the first life was on the land. Evolutionists tell us that life originated in the oceans because life on the land was rendered impossible by the lack of oxygen in the atmosphere and the harmful effects of ultraviolet radiation reaching the surface.

2. Evolutionists believe that fish and other marine organisms developed long before fruit trees. Genesis 1:11, 20, and 21 is a direct contradiction of this. Spores and fragments of woody plants, including those of pine trees, have been found in Cambrian rocks. Dr. Daniel Axelrod of the University of California at Davis has reported the finding of spores of 60 genera of woody plants in Cambrian strata. The Geologic Time Table does not have woody plants, such as the conifers, developing until 200 million years after the Cambrian period.

3. Geologists tell us that the sun and the moon are as old as the earth. Genesis 1:14-19 tells us that the sun and the moon were not made until the fourth day of creation. The light that was created on the first day came directly from God Himself (Psalms 104:2, Daniel 2:22, I Timothy 6:16, and Revelation 21:23). The Genesis account would have the plants created "one" day before the sun and the stars were created. If a day represents an indefinitely long period of time, some explanation must be made as to how the plants could have survived the long period without the energy of sunlight.

4. Geologists believe that insects came before birds, but the

Genesis account contradicts this. The "creeping things" (defined as insects in Leviticus, chapter 11) were made on the sixth day, and the birds were made the day before.

5. Geologists say that fish evolved hundreds of millions of years before birds. Genesis records that fish and birds were both made on the fifth day.

6. Evolutionists maintain the first marine life consisted only of a blob of complex chemicals. Genesis 1:20–21 says that God caused an abundance of marine life when He first created it. This is consistent with the fossil record. When life first appears in the Cambrian layers, it shows an abundance of life forms. Practically all phyla are evident, presenting a major mystery for the evolutionists. The fossil record fails to show the gradual evolution of life as predicted by the theory of evolution.

7. The Bible stresses several times that the life forms were created to reproduce "after their kind;" evolutionists postulate that present life types resulted from the slow ascent of all organisms from a common ancestor, that all life began with only one cell. The Bible tells us that the great sea monsters were among the first to be created.

8. Genesis 1:29 indicates that man was originally a vegetarian. Anthropologists maintain that the earliest men were not only hunters and meat eaters but probably were cannibals as well.

There are many other conflicts between the Biblical account and the evolution account of the origin of life that are not listed. But the point should be clear now that the two, creation and evolution, cannot be successfully combined into one harmonious theory; they are in complete opposition to each other. George Wald admitted that there are no third alternatives but that each person must decide between the only two: spontaneous generation of life (evolution) *or* the creation of life by a Divine Being.

Gap Theory

Another attempt to combine evolution with creation is the Gap Theory. But, like the Day-Age Theory, the Gap Theory is not actually taught by the Scriptures. This theory advocates that there was a very long and unrecorded period of time between Genesis 1:1 and 1:2. It further states that Genesis 1:2 would be better translated: "and the earth *became* without form and void." Those adhering to this theory support their position by referring to Isaiah 45:18 where it states:

PROBLEMS IN THE DAY-AGE THEORY

Spontaneous generation and organic evolution

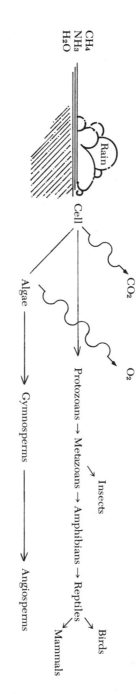

Divine Creation in six days

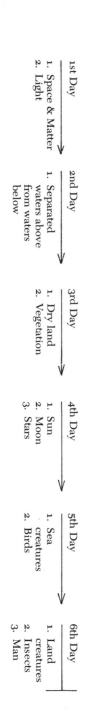

"For thus saith the Lord who created the heavens, God himself who formed the earth and made it; he hath established it, he created it not in vain, he formed it to be inhabited."

Gap theorists claim that the heaven and the earth of Genesis 1:1 were inhabited until a catastrophic event occurred. They believe that when Satan rebelled against God (see Isaiah, chapter 14), God cast Satan from heaven to the earth. God's perfect creation came to an end at that time. The Gap theorists believe that the Genesis account of creation is actually referring to God's re-creation of His previously perfect heaven and earth, having been made to be "void and without form" because of the fall of Satan.

The Gap Theory is laden with as many problems as is the Day-Age Theory. The Gap theorists have attempted to provide a plausible Biblical explanation for the fossil record which the evolutionists believe shows the earth's life forms as having developed through a progressive evoltionary ascent from the simple to the complex. Had the full evidence been presented in the first place, there would have been no need for Christians to rationalize the Biblical account of creation. There is actually no conflict with the observable fossil record and the Genesis record.

Consider just a few of the problems in attempting to combine evolution and creation by means of the Gap Theory:

1. The word "was" that is found in Genesis 1:2 comes from a regular Hebrew verb of being: *hayah*. The normal word for "became" is *haphak* and is not used in Genesis 1:2. Furthermore, the use of *waw* ("and") serves as a connective at the beginning of the second verse and does not lend its support to a "gap" allowing an immense period of time as having occurred between the first two verses in the Bible.

2. The word "void" in Genesis 1:2 implies that no living thing was present on the earth at that time. In the book of Job, chapter 26, the same word, *tohu*, is used and translated as "empty." This word simply means that the world was uninhabited at the time of Genesis 1:2. In no way does it imply that the world had been previously inhabited.

3. In Genesis 2:3, absolutely all of God's work of both "creating" and "making" all things—the heavens and the earth and all within them ("all that is in them . . . " according to Exodus 20:11)—was accomplished in just six days. There is absolutely no portion of scripture that supports the hypothesis of a previous creation.

4. There is no scriptural evidence that Satan's fall in heaven produced a cataclysm on Earth. The fact that God's estimate of "every-

thing" in the earth as "very good" after His six days of creative activity would seem to imply that Satan's fall had not yet occurred. Furthermore, it was not Satan's fall that brought "death" and "disorder" to the earth, but the sin of one man, Adam. In I Corinthians 15:21 we read, " . . . by man cometh death."

There is just no way the Word of God can be "watered down" so that it will parallel the philosophy of the world. There seems to be no other alternative. You must either accept the Biblical account of creation, thus rejecting the doctrine of evolution, *or* you must accept the doctrine of evolution and reject the Biblical account of creation. You cannot successfully combine the two.

How Could They Have Known?

For thousands of years wise men have attempted to count the stars in the heavens. Before the invention of the telescope in the 17th century, the number of stars was thought to have been determined. The great Ptolemy (330 BC) gave the number as 1,056. Tyco Brahe (1546–1601 AD) catalogued 777, the perfect divine number. And Kepler (1571–1630) listed the number as 1,005.

With the invention of the telescope, men began to realize that it might be impossible to count the stars of heaven. The further the telescopes reached into the distant regions of the universe, there were just more stars. We now know that there are billions of galaxies throughout the universe. In our own Milky Way galaxy there are an estimated 100 billion stars. If each galaxy contains the same number of stars, then the stars of heaven cannot be counted.

In the book of Jeremiah, written around 600 BC, we read that "the host of heaven cannot be numbered" (Jeremiah 33:22). This fact was discovered with the invention of the telescope. But how could Jeremiah have known this fact some 2,000 years before the telescope?

The Bible certainly is not a scientific book. Its purpose is clearly a message of an omniscient, omnipresent, omnipotent and eternal God. Nevertheless, the Bible has many scientific facts that have only been discovered in comparatively recent years. The question that all readers of the Bible should ask is, How could the writers of the Scriptures be so knowledgeable about details only recently discovered? I believe the answer is found in this Book of Truth. "The whole Bible was given to us by inspiration from God and is useful to teach us what is true . . . " (II Timothy 3:16).

Upon what does the earth rest? This question has been asked by almost every major civilization that has existed. The answers are as varied as the people asking the question. When Moses penned the Pentateuch, the Hindus held to the belief that "the earth is borne by four elephants standing on a tortoise's back." Others would have had the god Atlas holding up the earth.

But in the Book of Job, it is written: "He . . . hangeth the earth upon nothing." (Job 26:7) This certainly sounds like 20th century science! The attraction of gravity is obviously involved in accounting for the earth's steady position as it orbits the sun. But this really explains little. No one knows exactly what gravity is or why it is. It is merely a term coined to explain certain observable phenomena. There is little that modern science can add to or take away from the age-old observation by Job that God has hung the earth upon nothing. But, how could Job have known this thousands of years ago?

Since recorded history, men have described what they believed to be the true shape of the earth. It has had many forms: a bowl, a cube, a flat disk, and so on. By the time the astronauts turned their cameras back on Earth from the vicinity of the moon, it was well established that the earth was a nearly perfect sphere. But Isaiah recorded in the 8th century B.C. that the earth was a sphere—almost three thousand years ago! "It is He who sitteth upon the circle of the earth." The word translated "circle" comes from the Hebrew *khug*. Bible scholars tell us that a more accurate translation of this word would imply "sphericity" or "roundness." But how could Isaiah have known?

Jesus Christ also implied that the earth is a sphere when He spoke of His Second Coming. In Luke 17:31, it is written: "On that day, let him who is on the housetops . . . likewise let him who is in the field not turn back." This reference is to activities that are performed during daylight hours. One can certainly say that Christ implied that His return would be during the day. But, in Luke 17:34, Christ further adds: "I tell you, in that night, there will be two men in one bed; one will be taken and the other left." Here the reference indicates that His return will be during the night. This can only happen if the earth is a sphere. The Bible has recorded without a doubt that the earth is a sphere, but only in comparatively recent times have men come to accept this as the truth.

The well-known Bible critic, Robert Greene Ingersoll (1833–1899), used this very concept in hopes of disproving the reliability of the Bible. He made reference to Revelation 11:3–14 in which is recorded the murder of Christ's two witnesses during the last days before his return. Here it is recorded that the whole world would be able to view the bodies of these two men as they lay in the streets of Jerusalem for three-and-a-half days:

> And their dead bodies shall lie in the street of the great city, which spiritually is called Sodom and Egypt, where also our Lord was crucified. And they of the people and kindreds and tongues and nations shall see their dead bodies three days and a half, and shall not suffer their dead bodies to be put in graves. (Rev. 11:8,9)

Ingersoll was convinced that people living on the opposite side of the world would never be able to see these bodies. He therefore concluded that the Bible was fallible. We should not be too harsh on Ingersoll for he had no way of knowing that in the very next century men would position satellites above the earth that would allow "those on the other side of the earth" to observe events happening live some 12,000 miles away. I cannot help but think of Ingersoll when I turn on my television set to watch an event occurring on the opposite side of the globe. Because of these satellites I have watched the Munich Olympics live, the many Apollo splash-downs, and major world events such as the meeting between Egyptian President Sadat and Israeli President Begin.

We can understand that Ingersoll had no way of knowing about these satellites. But how can we explain away the fact that John, the writer of the Book of the Revelation, knew that the whole world will be able to observe this single event at the very moment it takes place? John lived almost two thousand years ago.

A final bit of interesting information deals with the sun's orbital path. In Psalms 19:6 we find written: "His going forth is from the end of the heaven, and his circuit unto the ends of it; and there is nothing hid from the heat thereof." The sun is the object of this reference. At first, one may incorrectly conclude that this reference implies that the sun orbits the earth. It was not until the time of Nicolas Copernicus the famous Polish astronomer, (1473–1543), that the world was finally convinced that it is the earth that orbits the sun, not the other way.

With better understanding of the cosmic pathways, we realize today that the psalmist was correct. We know that the sun, with the entire solar system, actually does move through space at the tremendous speed of 600,000 miles per hour in a gigantic orbit within the Milky Way galaxy. This orbit is so large that it requires an estimated 200 million years to complete just a single trip.

Modern astronomers have been able to obtain such information and knowledge only within recent years. How could the psalmist David have known about the sun's orbital path?

EPILOGUE

Julian Huxley accepted the theory of evolution because he believed that "Darwin removed the whole idea of God as creator." He felt that Darwin had demonstrated through natural selection "that no supernatural designer was needed." Aldous Huxley believed that the doctrine of evolution was essential if he was to be successful in developing his philosophy of meaninglessness. Dr. D.M.S. Watson was convinced that the theory of evolution was "universally accepted not because it can be proved by logically coherent evidence to be true, but because the only alternative, special creation, is clearly incredible."

Some accept evolution because they believe that the majority of the evidence supports evolution. Almost all media tend to lead the general public into accepting evolution as a fact. But I believe the public has been misled. I once heard a speaker with a doctorate explain to his audience that he accepted the theory of evolution as a fact ever since science had been able to create life!

Evolution is admittedly outside empirical science. It is not subject to observation or experimentation. Paul Ehrlich admits that evolutionary ideas "have become part of an evolutionary dogma accepted by most of us as part of our training." Most people accept evolution simply because they have been told to accept it.

Still, there are those who accept evolution because they are afraid not to accept it. "Most enlightened people now accept" the theory of evolution. If you do not accept evolution, you cannot be considered "enlightened" by some people. Furthermore, " . . . the fact of evolution could be denied only by an abandonment of reason." Who wants to be thought of as having abandoned his reason? And then, " . . . it is another thing to be told (and have to believe) that we are products . . . " of evolution. According to some, you don't even have a choice in the question of the origin of life. The Humanist Association has emphatically stated that "there are no alternatives to the theory of evolution."

I recently read a newspaper article that disclaimed the six-day creation as given to us in Genesis. According to Oxford Professor Don James Barr, "the Genesis story of creation is no longer held to be literally true by conservative Bible scholars." Why? Because "the scientific evidence for the beginnings of the world are too strong for a literal interpretation of Scripture on this point . . . " (London Telegraph Foreign Service, February 18, 1978). Again, reference is made to scientific evidence which does not really exist.

The modernist certainly has not been able to prove his theory of evolution—nor to disprove special creation. But in a type of psychological warfare, he has been able to dupe thousands into accepting evolution with the threat that if you don't, you must not be intelligent.

If one is truly to be an evolutionist, then he must also be an atheist as well. I realize that some will disagree with this statement, but in evolution there is no room or need for God. Julian Huxley clearly stated that "evolutionary man" created his own god—not the other way around.

I recall a conversation I once had with a university professor, an acclaimed evolutionist, who tried to explain how one need not be an atheist just because one is an evolutionist. He proceeded to explain how God, who had nothing to do with the creation of the universe or of life, was there simply to enrich our lives and to provide us with our rich religious heritage. He explained that each person was responsible for developing his own concept of divinity; the Christians developed Christ into a God, the Jews had Jehovah, the Moslems had Mohammed and so on. In conclusion, he admitted that he did not personally believe in God, but that each person has the right to choose whatever religion that pleases him. However, he did not consider himself an atheist.

Have I been able to convince you that evolution is false, or that creation is true? I do not think so. But I hope I have provided enough evidence to suggest to you that the creationist has as strong, if not stronger, a case as does the evolutionist. However, the Biblical account of creation must eventually be accepted by faith—but the theory of evolution must also be eventually accepted by faith.

If you followed the suggestion in the Introduction to make a list of ten evidences you believe support evolution, how did the list hold up? Is the evidence as strong as you thought it was? If not, then I hope your search for truth will be as rewarding to you as mine has been to me.

Should you choose evolution, then you should be aware of what you have chosen:

1. Spontaneous generation—that life can arise from the non-living
2. That life is non-purposive, just a freak chemical accident
3. That all systems, if left alone, will tend to improve themselves in spite of the second law of thermodynamics
4. That species tend to develop into new and improved species by means of genetic mutations
5. That you are just an animal and part of a system devoid of meaning and purpose
6. That to completely accept evolution, you must be an atheist—there is no room for God in evolution.

However, should you choose to accept special creation, then you will have chosen a life with purpose and meaning. But more important than that, you will have acknowledged that you have a Creator.

REFERENCE

Chapter One:
1. John W. Klotz, "Creationist Viewpoint," in *Symposium on Creation*, edited by Henry Morris, (Baker Book House, Grand Rapids, Michigan, 1968) p. 47 (used by permission).
2. Philip H. Abelson as quoted by *Acts and Facts*, Vol. 6, # 9, September, 1977, p. ii (used by permission).
3. Theodosius Dobzhansky, "On Methods of Evolutionary Biology and Anthropology," *American Scientist*, Vol. 45, 1957, p. 388.
4. George Wald, "The Origin of Life," *Scientific American*, August, 1954.
5. D. M. S. Watson, "Adaptation," *Nature*, Vol. 124, 1929, p. 233 (used by permission).
6. Loren Eisely, *The Immense Journey*, (Random House, New York, 1957) p. 199 (used by permission).
7. Thomas G. Barnes, "A Scientific Alternative to Evolution" in *Scientific Studies In Special Creation*, edited by W. E. Lammerts, (Presbyterian and Reformed Publishing Co., 1971) p. 330 (used by permission).
8. Julian Huxley, Associated Press Dispatch, November 27, 1959.
9. Paul Ehrlich and L. C. Birch, "Evolutionary History and Population Biology," *Nature*, Vol. 214, 1967, p. 352.

Chapter Two:
1. W. R. Thompson, "Introduction" to *Origin of Species*, (Everyman's Library, New York, 1956)

Chapter Three:
1. Henry Morris, *A Biblical Manual on Science and Creation*, (Institute for Creation Research, San Diego, Ca., 1972) p. 7 (used by permission)
2. Gerard P. Kuiper as quoted by John C. Whitcomb, *The Origin of the Solar System*, (Presbyterian and Reformed Publishing Company, Pa., 1971) p. 12 (used by permission)
3. W. M. Smart as quoted by John C. Whitcomb, *ibid*, p. 16 (used by permission)
4. William A. Fowler, "The Origin of the Elements," *Scientific American*, September, 1965, p. 85

5. Fred Hoyle as quoted by John C. Whitcomb, *ibid*, p. 23 (used by permission)
6. Henry Morris, *Scientific Creationism*, (Creation-Life Publishers, San Diego, Ca., 1974) p. 152 (used by permission)

Chapter Four
1. From a UPI article dated February 23, 1977
2. R. A. Deering, "Ultraviolet Radiation and Nucleic Acid," *Scientific American*, December, 1962
3. George G. Simpson and W. S. Beck, *Life: An Introduction to Biology*, 2nd edition, (Harcourt, Brace and World, Inc., 1965) p. 65 (used by permission)
4. Larry Butler as quoted by Henry Morris, *Scientific Creationism*, (Creation-Life Publishers, San Diego, 1974) p. 65 (used by permission)
5. Szent-Gyorgyi as quoted by Jerry Bergman, "Albert Szent-Gyorgyi's Theory of Synthropy and Creationism," *Acts and Facts*, Vol. 6, December 1977, p. ii (used by permission)
6. George Simpson, *ibid*, p. 750 (used by permission)
7. Ernst J. Öpik, "Climate and the Changing Sun," *Scientific American*, June, 1958
8. Gerrit L. Verschuur, "The Gaea Hypothesis," *Griffith Observer*, Vol. 41, December, 1977, p. 6 (used by permission)
9. Gerrit L. Verschuur, *ibid*, p. 3 (used by permission)

Chapter Five
1. George Wald, "The Origin of Life," *Scientific American*, August, 1954
2. Harold F. Blum as quoted by Thomas G. Barnes, "A Scientific Alternative to Evolution," in *Scientific Studies in Special Creation*, Walter E. Lammerts, editor, (Presbyterian and Reformed Publishing Company, 1971) p. 334 (used by permission)
3. George Wald, *ibid*
4. Duane T. Gish, *Speculations and Experiments Related to Theories on the Origin of Life, a Critique*, (Institute For Creation Research, San Diego, 1972) p. 6 (used by permission)
5. Duane T. Gish, *ibid*, p. 9 (used by permission)
6. A. E. Wilder Smith as quoted by T. Robert Ingram in the Foreword to *A Symposium on Creation*, by Henry Morris, *et al*, (Baker Book House, Grand Rapids, Michigan, 1968) (used by permission)
7. George G. Simpson and W. S. Beck, *Life: An Introduction to Biology*, 2nd edition, (Harcourt, Brace and World, Inc., 1965) p. 754 (used by permission)
8. Henry Morris, *Scientific Creationism*, (Creation-Life Publishers, San Diego, 1974) p. 49–50 (used by permission)
9. Duane T. Gish, *ibid*, p. 34 (used by permission)

10. Duane T. Gish, *ibid*, p. 34 (used by permission)
11. Henry Morris, *ibid*, p. 49 (used by permission)

Chapter Six
1. Sir Julian Huxley as quoted by Henry Morris, *Scientific Creationism*, (Creation-Life Publishers, San Diego, 1974) p. 11 (used by permission)
2. L. Harrison Matthews in the Introduction to Darwin's *Origin of Species*, (J. M. Dent and Sons, Ltd., London, 1971) p. x
3. Harold L. Shapiro, "Organic Evolution," *Collier's Encyclopedia* (1970), p. 477 (used by permission)
4. *ibid*, p. 479 (used by permission)
5. Information taken from *Genetic Conditions*, (California State Department of Education, Sacramento, 1977) p. 33
6. *ibid*. p. 34 (used by permission)
7. James F. Crow, "Ionizing Radiation and Evolution," *Scientific American*, September, 1959
8. *ibid*

Chapter Seven
1. Holoworth in *The Mammoth and the Flood*, p. 351 as quoted by Alfred M. Rehwinkel, *The Flood*, (Concordia Publishing House, St. Louis, 1967) p. 214 (used by permission)
2. Henry Morris, *Scientific Creationism*, (Creation-Life Publishers, San Diego, 1974) pp. 87–88 (used by permission)
3. Walter E. Lammerts as quoted by Henry Morris, *The Twilight of Evolution*, (Baker Book House, Grand Rapids, Michigan, 1963) p. 54 (used by permission)
4. T. Neville George, "Fossils in Evolutionary Perspective," *Science Progress*, Vol. 48. (January 1960) pp. 1,3
5. Fred J. Meldau, *Why We Believe In Creation, Not Evolution*, (Christian Victory Publishing Company, Denver, 1959) p. 15
6. Daniel Axelrod, *Science*, Vol. 128, 1958, p. 7 (used by permission)
7. George Simpson and W. S. Beck, *Life: An Introduction to Biology*, 2nd edition, (Harcourt, Brace and World, Inc., 1965) p. 760 (used by permission)
8. ———, "Puzzling Out Man's Ascent," *Time Magazine*, (November 7, 1977) p. 77 (used by permission)
9. ———, *Acts and Facts*, Vol. 6, # 12, (Institute for Creation Reserach, December, 1977) used by permission
10. Henry Morris, *A Biblical Manual on Science and Creation*, (Institute for Creation Research, San Diego, 1972) pp. 17–18 (used by permission)
11. Carl O. Dunbar, *Historical Geology*, (John Wiley and Sons, New York, 1960) p. 18 (used by permission)

12. Donald W. Patten, "The Ice Epoch" in *Symposium on Creation* by Henry Morris and others, (Baker Book House, Grand Rapids, Michigan, 1968) p. 129 (used by permission)
13. William J. Meister as quoted by Melvin A. Cook, *Why Not Creation*, (Presbyterian and Reformed Publishing Co., 1970) pp. 186–7 (used by permission)

Chapter Eight
1. Melvin A. Cook, "Do Radiological 'Clocks' Need Repair?" in *Scientific Studies in Special Creation*, Walter E. Lammerts, editor, (Presbyterian and Reformed Publishing Co., 1971), pp. 79–97
2. *ibid*, p. 79 (used by permission)
3. George Simpson and W. S. Beck, *Life, An Introduction to Biology*, (Harcourt, Brace and World Inc., 1965) p. 750 (used by permission)

Chapter Nine
1. Norman D. Newell, "Crises in the History of life," *Scientific American*, February, 1963

Chapter Ten
1. George Simpson and W. S. Beck, *Life: An Introduction to Biology*, 2nd edition, (Harcourt, Brace and World, Inc., 1965) p. 750 (used by permission)
2. *ibid*, pp. 758–9 (used by permission)

Chapter Eleven
1. George Simpson and W. S. Beck, *Life: An Introduction to Biology*, 2nd edition, (Harcourt, Brace and World, Inc., 1965) p. 757 (used by permission)
2. James W. Valentine, "The Present is the Key to the Present," *Journal of Geological Education*, Vol. 14, April, 1966, pp. 59–60 (used by permission)
3. Edgar B. Heylmun, "Should We Teach Uniformitarianism?" *Journal of Geological Education*, Vol. 19, January, 1971, p. 36 (used by permission)
4. John E. Whitcomb, *The World that Perished*, (Baker Book House, Grand Rapids, Michigan, 1973) p. 23 (used by permission)
5. *ibid*, p. 32 (used by permission)
6. *ibid*, p. 35 (used by permission)
7. *ibid*, p. 39 (used by permission)
8. *ibid*, p. 72 (used by permission)
9. *ibid*, p. 76 (used by permission)
10. Johannes Riem as quoted by Alfred M. Rehwinkel, *The Flood*, (Concordia Publishing House, St. Louis, Mo., 1951) p. 129 (used by permission)

11. Hugh Miller as quoted by Alfred M. Rehwinkel, *ibid*, p. 130 (used by permission)
12. Rehwinkel, *ibid*, p. 135 (used by permission)

Chapter Twelve
1. Duane T. Gish, *The Fossils Say No*, (Creation-Life Publishers, San Diego, 1973), p. 77 (used by permission)
2. "Puzzling Out Man's Ascent," *Time Magazine*, November 7, 1977, p. 69 (used by permission)
3. *Ibid.*, p. 69 (used by permission)
4. *Ibid.*, p. 67 (used by permission)
5. Gish, *ibid.*, p. 82 (used by permission)
6. Duane T. Gish, "Richard Leakey's Skull 1470," *Acts and Facts*, February, 1974, p. i (used by permission)
7. *Ibid.*, p. i (used by permission)